Aircraft
Frequencies
& Guide Book

Second Edition

Graham Duke

First published 1995 as *Air to Ground Radio Frequencies*
This Edition 1997
Reprinted 1998

ISBN 0 7110 2566 5

Material on aircraft recognition reproduced from *abc Civil Airliner Recognition* and *abc Light Aircraft Recognition* by Peter R. March. Both copyright © Ian Allan Ltd.

Published by Ian Allan Publishing: an imprint of Ian Allan Publishing Ltd, Terminal House, Station Approach, Shepperton, Surrey TW17 8AS.

Printed by Ian Allan Printing Ltd, 'Riverdene', Molesey Road, Hersham, Surrey KT12 4RG.

Front cover:
Photograph supplied by Steepletone Products Ltd

Back Cover:
PA-28R Cherokee Arrow (G-AWFK) owned by Steepletone Products Ltd.
Photograph supplied by Steepletone Products Ltd

CONTENTS

AREA MAP

IMPORTANT NOTE

THE AREAS USED IN THIS GUIDE ARE FOR CONVENIENCE OF DISPLAYING INFORMATION AND SHOULD NOT BE REGARDED AS ACCURATE AND NEVER USED FOR NAVIGATION.

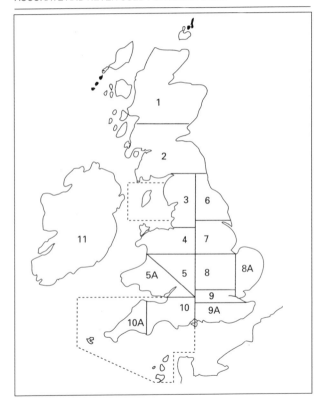

INTRODUCTION

The number of flights using UK airspace has been steadily increasing for years and there is every indication that it will continue to do so, well in to the new century.

This, of course, has placed a very considerable strain on the air traffic control system which is required to handle the traffic safely and expeditiously. Since the amount of airspace is more or less fixed, the capacity to deal with the extra flights is being achieved by improved international co-operation across Europe and better use of the latest technology which can help to ease the controllers' workload.

Many new routes have been introduced, some of which follow 'great circle' tracks (the shortest distance between two points) rather than the traditional system of using ground-based radio navigation transmitters. At the same time, in order to ensure that controllers do not become overloaded, extra control areas (sectors) have been added, some of which divide the traffic responsibility horizontally – in other words aircraft at different levels are controlled by different control teams using separate radio frequencies.

One of the most important projects for the Civil Aviation Authority is the construction and implementation of a new control centre at Swanwick, near Fareham in Hampshire, which is likely to become operational in 1999. The Swanwick Centre will use the world's most advanced systems to deal with air traffic well into the 21st century. A new Scottish Centre is also planned.

Another major change, initially in the busy southeast of England, will be the reduction in frequency steps for VHF (civilian) aeronautical radio. The present steps between channels of 25kHz will be reduced to 8.33kHz steps, thereby trebling the number of available frequencies.

On the other hand, in future years messages between ground stations and aircraft will be in the form of digital datalink, with no voice transmissions. This system is already in use for oceanic clearances and for route clearances (to a limited extent) at Gatwick.

Air traffic communications utilise three separate systems: Very High Frequency (VHF), Ultra High Frequency (UHF) and High Frequency (HF), also known as Short Wave.

Generally, VHF is used by civil traffic and some military flights. UHF is exclusively used by military aircraft. Both these systems operate over populated areas of the world. HF is used by all aircraft, and is a long range system operated over oceanic regions and sparsely populated areas of the world.

VHF and UHF are 'line of sight' transmissions, meaning that messages from high flying aircraft can usually be heard at a range of around 100 miles or greater. Ground transmissions, on the other hand, will only be heard when the receiver is relatively close to a ground transmitter or at an airport. The chances are, therefore, that in many areas of the UK the aircraft messages will be heard but not the controllers' responses.

A system of airways and upper air routes exists across the UK and Europe. These are generally based on radio navigation beacons on the ground, each with a unique name identifier and broadcast radio signal. Charts depicting these routes can be purchased from the Royal Air Force or from Aerad, at the following addresses:

Royal Air Force
No 1 AIDU
RAF Northolt
West End Road
Ruislip
Middlesex HA4 6NG

Racal Avionics Ltd
Aeronautical Services Group
Hersham House
Lyon Road
Walton-on-Thames
Surrey KT12 3PU

Finally, it is necessary to advise of the legal position concerning airband listening.

The receipt of any radio transmission for which the listener does not have a licence is illegal. The act of listening itself constitutes an offence, and it is not necessary to make use of the information (often a common misunderstanding) to be breaking the law.

Having frequencies programmed into a scanning receiver may be used as evidence by the authorities as an intention to listen, although this area of law is less clear and the enforcement agencies seem to turn a blind eye to airband listening.

Nevertheless, you will still be breaking the law if you listen to aircraft messages, so be warned.

ABBREVIATIONS USED IN THIS GUIDE

ABBREVIATION	REMARKS
A/C	AIRCRAFT
ACC	AREA CONTROL CENTRE
AFIS	AERODROME FLIGHT INFORMATION SERVICE
AG RADIO	AIR TO GROUND RADIO. NORMALLY FOR INFORMATION ONLY AND NOT GIVING MANDATORY INSTRUCTIONS.
AM	AMPLITUDE MODULATION. A TYPE OF RADIO TRANSMISSION.
APP	APPROACH
ARR/Arr	ARRIVALS
ATCC	AIR TRAFFIC CONTROL CENTRE ALSO AREA & TERMINAL CONTROL CENTRE
ATIS	AUTOMATIC TERMINAL INFORMATION SERVICE
ATZ	AERODROME TRAFFIC ZONE
BDY	BOUNDARY
CAS	CONTROLLED AIRSPACE
CIV AF	CIVIL AIRFIELD. CAN VARY FROM LARGE AIRFIELD WITH OR WITHOUT HARD RUNWAYS TO ONE OR MORE GRASS STRIPS NORMALLY LICENSED.
CIV AP	MAJOR AIRPORT WITH SUBSTANTIAL NUMBER OF SCHEDULED SERVICES AND NAVIGATIONAL AIDS.
CTA	CONTROL AREA
CTR	CONTROL ZONE
DEP/dep	DEPARTURES
DIR	DIRECTOR
DME	DISTANCE MEASURING EQUIPMENT
DZ	DROPPING ZONE FOR PARACHUTING
FIR	FLIGHT INFORMATION REGION
FIS	FLIGHT INFORMATION SERVICE
FL	FLIGHT LEVEL
FLTS	FLIGHTS
FM	FREQUENCY MODULATION. A TYPE OF RADIO TRANSMISSION.
FREQ	FREQUENCY
GMC	GROUND MOVEMENT CONTROL
GMD	GROUND MOVEMENT CONTROL
GRND	GROUND MOVEMENT CONTROL
HELI	HELICOPTER
HELIPAD	HELICOPTER PAD
HF	HIGH FREQUENCY. TYPE OF RADIO TRANSMISSION.
HRS	HOURS

ABBREVIATION	REMARKS
IFR	INSTRUMENT FLIGHT RULES
ILS	INSTRUMENT LANDING SYSTEM
IMC	INSTRUMENT METEOROLOGICAL CONDITIONS
INFO	INFORMATION
INTL	INTERNATIONAL
KHz	KILOHERTZ (RADIO FREQUENCY MEASUREMENT)
LARS	LOWER AIRSPACE RADAR ADVISORY SERVICE
LJAO	LONDON JOINT AREA ORGANISATION
MACC	MILITARY AREA CONTROL CENTRE
MARS	MIDDLE AIRSPACE RADAR ADVISORY SERVICE
MATZ	MILITARY AERODROME TRAFFIC ZONE
MEDA	MILITARY EMERGENCY DIVERSION AERODROME
METRO	PILOT TO METRO VOICE
MHz	MEGAHERTZ (RADIO FREQUENCY MEASUREMENT)
MIL	MILITARY
MIL AF	MILITARY AIRFIELD. (VARIES FROM MAJOR AIRFIELD TO HELICOPTER PAD)
MOD	MINISTRY OF DEFENCE
MRSA	MANDATORY RADAR SERVICE AREA
NDB	NON DIRECTIONAL BEACON
OAC	OCEANIC AREA CONTROL
OACC	OCEANIC AREA CONTROL CENTRE
OPS	OPERATIONS
OR	ON REQUEST
PAR	PRECISION APPROACH RADAR (TALKDOWN)
PRI	PRIVATE
PRI AF	PRIVATE AIRFIELD. CAN VARY FROM MAJOR AIRFIELD SUCH AS WARTON DOWN TO A SINGLE GRASS FARM STRIP.
RAD	RADAR
REG	REGISTERED
RNWY	RUNWAY
SAR	SEARCH AND RESCUE
SOTA	SHANNON OCEANIC TRANSITION AREA
SRA or SRZ	AIRSPACE IN WHICH SPECIAL RULES APPLY
SRE	SURVEILLANCE RADAR ELEMENT
SSB	SINGLE SIDE BAND. A TYPE OF RADIO TRANSMISSION.
STN	STATION. USUALLY REFERS TO RADIO STATION, BUT COULD MEAN RAF AIRFIELD.
TCA	TERMINAL CONTROL AREA
TMA	TERMINAL CONTROL AREA
TWR	TOWER
UAS	UPPER AIRSPACE SERVICE
UHF	ULTRA HIGH FREQUENCY. TYPE OF RADIO TRANSMISSION.
UIR	UPPER INFORMATION REGION
UIS	UPPER INFORMATION SERVICE

ABBREVIATION	REMARKS
VFR	VISUAL FLIGHT RULES
VHF	VERY HIGH FREQUENCY. TYPE OF RADIO TRANSMISSION.
VMC	VISUAL METEOROLOGICAL CONDITIONS
VOLMET	METEOROLOGICAL INFORMATION FOR AIRCRAFT IN FLIGHT
VOR	VHF OMNIDIRECTIONAL RANGE (VHF BEACON)
VRP	VISUAL REFERENCE POINT

IMPORTANT NOTE

THE AREAS USED IN THIS GUIDE ARE FOR CONVENIENCE OF DISPLAYING INFORMATION AND SHOULD NOT BE REGARDED AS ACCURATE AND NEVER USED FOR NAVIGATION

IMPORTANT NOTES ON USE OF GUIDE AREAS

1) DATA THAT REFERS TO THE SERVICE AT EACH STATION IS AS
UP TO DATE AS CAN BE ASCERTAINED TO THE END OF 1997. WE
REGRET THAT THE COMPILER AND THE PUBLISHER CAN NOT BE
RESPONSIBLE FOR ERRORS OR OMISSIONS CAUSED BY ALTER-
ATIONS MADE BETWEEN THE TIME DATA BECAME AVAILABLE TO
THEM AND THE TIME OF GOING TO PRINT.

2) THE AREAS USED IN THIS GUIDE ARE PURELY ARBITRARY TO
ALLOW THE GUIDE USER TO LOCATE MOST SERVICES AVAIL-
ABLE IN THE AREAS TO BE LOCATED IN ADJACENT SECTIONS
OR PAGES.

3) AN AMENDMENT PAGE IS PROVIDED AT THE END OF EACH AREA
SECTION HEADED IN THE WAY OTHER SECTOR DATA IS PRE-
SENTED TO ENABLE THE GUIDE USER TO MAKE THEIR OWN
UPDATES AS THEY COME TO HAND.

4) THE SERVICE LISTED (EG. AN APPROACH OR RADAR FREQUEN-
CY MAY NOT BE AVAILABLE ON A 24 HOUR BASIS, OR EVEN
EVERY DAY). IN SOME CASES THIS APPLIES TO WHOLE AIR-
FIELDS, ESPECIALLY THE SMALL PRIVATELY OWNED AIRSTRIPS
AND WORKS OWNED FIELDS.

5) TACTICAL MILITARY UHF TRANSMISSIONS AND MOST PRIVATE
BUSINESS FREQUENCIES HAVE BEEN OMITTED TO AVOID
REPERCUSSIONS THAT MIGHT OCCUR BECAUSE OF MISUSE OF
THE INFORMATION TRANSMITTED AND ALSO THESE DO
CHANGE MORE FREQUENTLY THAN OTHER SERVICES.

HOW TO USE THIS GUIDE

The frequency information quoted in this guide covers civil and military airfields, control areas, airways and upper air routes, and is intended to be a basic guide for the airband listener. As aeronautical frequencies change from time to time, however, it is inevitable that some of the details will be out of date. Any changes can be noted on the amendment pages which follow each section.

Throughout the guide, VHF and UHF frequencies are given in accordance with the standard UK radiotelephony convention, whereby no more than two digits are quoted after the decimal point.

For example, 118.725 is spoken as *'one one eight decimal seven two'* and 135.275 is spoken as *'one three five decimal two seven'*. This will apply in all cases where the second digit after the decimal point is either *'2'* or *'7'* – for example, 123.92(5) or 123.97(5).

Where the second digit after the decimal point is zero, only the first digit is spoken – for example 129.600 is expressed as *'one two nine decimal six'*.

However, it is important to remember that when tuning an airband scanner, the full six figure frequency has to be selected.

In each section, several frequencies are quoted under the *'Zones and Airways'* heading covering airways and upper air routes. In general, only one or two frequencies will actually be in use. Others may be heard when the primary frequencies are unserviceable or when traffic is particularly heavy, requiring the sub-division of airspace sectors.

For your particular area of interest, it is suggested that all the frequencies are programmed into the scanner's memory. Operating the receiver in the scanning mode will soon identify those channels which are in use.

AREA 1

AIRFIELDS OF NORTH SCOTLAND

STATION	TYPE	FREQUENCY	SERVICE / REMARKS / CALL
UNST	CIV AP	130.35	TWR / APP
		123.45	OPS
		123.15	SUMBURGH RADAR
LERWICK (TINGWALL)	122.6	TWR / AG	PRI AF
SCATSCA	PRI AF	123,6	TWR / APP
		122.4	RADAR
FAIR ISLE	CIV AF	123.15	SUMBURGH APP
WHALSAY	CIV AF	123.15	SUMBURGH APP
SUMBURGH	CIV AP	118.25	TWR
		125.85	ATIS
		123.15	APP
		123.15	RAD
		130.05	RAD
NORTH RONALDSAY	CIV AF	118.3	KIRKWALL APP
EDAY	CIV AF	118.3	KIRKWALL APP
PAPA WESTRAY	CIV AP	118.3	KIRKWALL APP
WESTRAY	CIV AP	118.3	KIRKWALL APP
SANDAY	CIV AP	118.3	KIRKWALL APP
STRONSAY	CIV AP	118.3	KIRKWALL APP
KIRKWALL	CIV AP	118.3	TWR / APP
FLOTTA	PRI AF	122.15	AG RADIO
STORNAWAY	CIV AP	123.5	TWR / APP
		123.5	AFIS OUT OF TWR HRS
		362.3	KINLOSS APP
WICK	CIV AP	119.7	TWR
		130.37	FAR NORTH AG
INVERNESS	CIV AP	122.6	TWR / APP
		362.3	APP
TAIN RANGE	MIL RANGE	122.75	MIL RANGE AG
GARVIE	MIL RANGE	133.2	MIL RANGE AG
FEARN	PRI AF	122.75	TAIN RANGE RADIO

AREA 1

AIRFIELDS OF NORTH SCOTLAND

STATION	TYPE	FREQUENCY	SERVICE / REMARKS / CALL
KINLOSS	MIL AF	122.1	TWR
		119.35	APP / MATZ
		123.3	DIRECTOR
		123.3	DIR / PAR RAD / SRE
		336.35	TWR
		257.8	TWR
		376.65	APP
		362.3	APP
		358.47	OPS
		259.97	DIR
		311.32	DIR
		370.05	PAR RADAR
		376.52	PAR RADAR
DORNOCH	PRI AF	119.35	LOSSIEMOUTH APP
LOSSIEMOUTH	MIL AF	118.9	TWR
		122.1	TWR
		119.35	APP / MATZ / LARS
		123.3	APP
		123.3	PAR RADAR
		337.75	TWR
		299.4	GRND
		376.65	APP /LARS
		362.3	APP
		258.85	DEPARTURES
		259.97	DIR
		311.32	DIR
		250.05	PAR RADAR
		312.4	PAR RADAR
INSCH	PRI AF	129.82	AG RADIO
		120.4	ABERDEEN APP
ABERDEEN	CIV AP	118.1	TWR
		121.7	GRND
		114.3	ATIS (ARRIVAL INFO)
		121.85	ATIS (DEPARTURE INFO)
		120.4	APP (NORTH SEA RAD)
		128.3	NORTH SEA RADAR
		121.25	NORTH SEA RADAR
		353.55	APP / NORTH SEA RADAR

AREAS 1 & 2

ZONES & AIRWAYS OF SCOTLAND

FREQUENCY	CALL	SERVICE
119.87	SCOTTISH INFORMATION	EAST
127.27	SCOTTISH INFORMATION	WEST
131.3	SCOTTISH INFORMATION	NORTH
125.72	VOLMET (SCOTTISH)	WEATHER
128.67	PENNINE RADAR	RADAR SERVICE
126.3	SCOTTISH CONTROL	TMA VIA TALLA & EDINBURGH
126.25	SCOTTISH CONTROL	TMA VIA GLASGOW & NEW GALLOWAY
123.37	SCOTTISH CONTROL	AIRWAYS CONTROL — A1, A2, A25, B2, B3, B4, B226, L602
123.77	SCOTTISH CONTROL	AIRWAYS CONTROL — A1, A2, A25, B2, B3, B4, B226, L602
124.5	SCOTTISH CONTROL	AIRWAYS CONTROL — A1, A2, A25, B2, B3, B4, B226, L602
124.82	SCOTTISH CONTROL	AIRWAYS CONTROL — A1, A2, A25, B2, B3, B4, B226, L602
126.3	SCOTTISH CONTROL	AIRWAYS CONTROL — A1, A2, A25, B2, B3, B4, B226, L602
123.77	SCOTTISH CONTROL	ADVISORY ROUTES — A1D, B2D, N552D, N553D, N562D, N573D, W3D, W4D, W5D, W6D, W911D, W928D, W958D
124.5	SCOTTISH CONTROL	ADVISORY ROUTES — A1D, B2D, N552D, N553D, N562D, N573D, W3D, W4D, W5D, W6D, W911D, W928D, W958D
126.25	SCOTTISH CONTROL	ADVISORY ROUTES — A1D, B2D, N552D, N553D, N562D, N573D, W3D, W4D, W5D, W6D, W911D, W928D, W958D
127.27	SCOTTISH CONTROL	ADVISORY ROUTES — A1D, B2D, N552D, N553D, N562D, N573D, W3D, W4D, W5D, W6D, W911D, W928D, W958D
133.67	SCOTTISH CONTROL	ADVISORY ROUTES — A1D, B2D, N552D, N553D, N562D, N573D, W3D, W4D, W5D, W6D, W911D, W928D, W958D

AREAS 1 & 2

ZONES & AIRWAYS OF SCOTLAND

FREQUENCY	CALL	SERVICE
125.67	SCOTTISH CONTROL	UPPER AIR ROUTES — UA1, UA2, UA25, UB2, UB3, UB4, UG11, UH70, UH71, UL602, UL613, UN517, UN537, UN545, UN550, UN551, UN552, UN559, UN560, UN561, UN562, UN563, UN569, UN570, UN571, UN572, UN573, UN580, UN581, UN583, UN584, UN590, UN591, UN593, UN601, UN603, UN610, UN612, UN614, UN615, UR23, UR38, UW502, UW532, UW534,UW536, UW536, UW538, UW701
126.25	SCOTTISH CONTROL	UPPER AIR ROUTES — UA1, UA2, UA25, UB2, UB3, UB4, UG11, UH70, UH71, UL602, UL613, UN517, UN537, UN545, UN550, UN551, UN552, UN559, UN560, UN561, UN562, UN563, UN569, UN570, UN571, UN572, UN573, UN580, UN581, UN583, UN584, UN590, UN591, UN593, UN601, UN603, UN610, UN612, UN614, UN615, UR23, UR38, UW502, UW532, UW534,UW536, UW536, UW538, UW701
129.22	SCOTTISH CONTROL	UPPER AIR ROUTES — UA1, UA2, UA25, UB2, UB3, UB4, UG11, UH70, UH71, UL602, UL613, UN517, UN537, UN545, UN550, UN551, UN552, UN559, UN560, UN561, UN562, UN563, UN569, UN570, UN571, UN572, UN573, UN580, UN581, UN583, UN584, UN590, UN591, UN593, UN601, UN603, UN610, UN612, UN614, UN615, UR23, UR38, UW502, UW532, UW534,UW536, UW536, UW538, UW701

AREAS 1 & 2

ZONES & AIRWAYS OF SCOTLAND

FREQUENCY	CALL	SERVICE
132.72	SCOTTISH CONTROL	UPPER AIR ROUTES — UA1, UA2, UA25, UB2, UB3, UB4, UG11, UH70, UH71, UL602, UL613, UN517, UN537, UN545, UN550, UN551, UN552, UN559, UN560, UN561, UN562, UN563, UN569, UN570, UN571, UN572, UN573, UN580, UN581, UN583, UN584, UN590, UN591, UN593, UN601, UN603, UN610, UN612, UN614, UN615, UR23, UR38, UW502, UW532, UW534,UW536, UW536, UW538, UW701
133.67	SCOTTISH CONTROL	UPPER AIR ROUTES — UA1, UA2, UA25, UB2, UB3, UB4, UG11, UH70, UH71, UL602, UL613, UN517, UN537, UN545, UN550, UN551, UN552, UN559, UN560, UN561, UN562, UN563, UN569, UN570, UN571, UN572, UN573, UN580, UN581, UN583, UN584, UN590, UN591, UN593, UN601, UN603, UN610, UN612, UN614, UN615, UR23, UR38, UW502, UW532, UW534,UW536, UW536, UW538, UW701
134.77	SCOTTISH CONTROL	UPPER AIR ROUTES — UA1, UA2, UA25, UB2, UB3, UB4, UG11, UH70, UH71, UL602, UL613, UN517, UN537, UN545, UN550, UN551, UN552, UN559, UN560, UN561, UN562, UN563, UN569, UN570, UN571, UN572, UN573, UN580, UN581, UN583, UN584, UN590, UN591, UN593, UN601, UN603, UN610, UN612, UN614, UN615, UR23, UR38, UW502, UW532, UW534,UW536, UW536, UW538, UW701
249.47	SCOTTISH MILITARY	UPPER, MIDDLE & LOWER AIRSPACE SERVICE
134.3	SCOTTISH MILITARY	UPPER, MIDDLE & LOWER AIRSPACE SERVICE

AREAS 1 & 2

ZONES & AIRWAYS OF SCOTLAND

FREQUENCY	CALL	SERVICE
129.95	VIKING APPROACH	NORTH SEA LOWER AIRSPACE ADVISORY & FLIGHT INFORMATION SERVICES
126.1	SUMBURGH RADAR	NORTH SEA LOWER AIRSPACE ADVISORY & FLIGHT INFORMATION SERVICES
123.15	SUMBURGH RADAR	NORTH SEA LOWER AIRSPACE ADVISORY & FLIGHT INFORMATION SERVICES
121.25	ABERDEEN RADAR	NORTH SEA LOWER AIRSPACE ADVISORY & FLIGHT INFORMATION SERVICES
134.1	ABERDEEN RADAR	NORTH SEA LOWER AIRSPACE ADVISORY & FLIGHT INFORMATION SERVICES
135.17	ABERDEEN INFORMATION	NORTH SEA LOWER AIRSPACE ADVISORY & FLIGHT INFORMATION SERVICES

AREA 2

AIRFIELDS OF SOUTH EAST SCOTLAND

STATION	TYPE	FREQUENCY	SERVICE / REMARKS / CALL
PERTH (SCONE)	CIV AF	119.8	TWR
		122.3	APP
DUNDEE	CIV AF	122.9	TWR / APP
ERROL	PRI AF	123.45	DZ CONTROL ERROL
		122.3	PERTH APP
		126.5	LEUCHARS APP
		122.9	DUNDEE APP
KINROSS	PRI AF	119.87	SCOTTISH INFORMATION
FIFE (GLENROTHES)	CIV AF	130.45	AG RADIO
LEUCHARS	MIL AF	122.1	TWR
		123.3	PAR / DIR / SRE
		362.3	APP
		285.02	OPS
		292.47	DIR

AREA 2

AIRFIELDS OF SOUTH EAST SCOTLAND

STATION	TYPE	FREQUENCY	SERVICE / REMARKS / CALL
LEUCHARS (continued)		370.07	PAR RADAR
		259.92	PAR RADAR
LEITH HELIPAD	CIV PAD	122.5	AG RADIO
		121.2	EDINBURGH APP
EDINBURGH	CIV AP	118.7	TWR / APP
		121.75	GRND
		132.07	ATIS
		121.2	APP / RAD
		130.4	FOR GLIDERS IN ATZ
		128.97	APP AS DIRECTED
		257.8	TWR / GRND
		362.3	RADAR
ST KILDA	MIL PAD	128.1	AG RADIO
BENBECULA	CIV AP	119.2	TWR / APP / AFIS
BARRA	CIV AP	130.65	AG RADIO / LOGANAIR
ISLE OF SKYE (BROADFORD)	CIV AP	130.65	AG RADIO / LOGANAIR
PLOCKTON	CIV AF	122.37	AG RADIO
KYLE (RN)	MIL RANGE	130.65	AG RADIO
TIREE	CIV AP	122.7	AFIS
COLONSAY (MACHRINS)	CIV AF	122.7	TIREE INFORMATION

AREA 2

AIRFIELDS OF WEST SCOTLAND

STATION	TYPE	FREQUENCY	SERVICE / REMARKS / CALL
COLL (BALLARD)	PRI AF	122.7	TIREE INFORMATION
GLENFORSA (MULL)	CIV AF	124.5	SCOTTISH INFORMATION
OBAN	CIV AF	130.1	AG RADIO (GLIDERS)
		129.82	AG (MICROLIGHTS)

AREA 2

AIRFIELDS OF WEST SCOTLAND

STATION	TYPE	FREQUENCY	SERVICE / REMARKS / CALL
GIGHA	PRI AF	123.05	AG RADIO
		125.9	MACHRIOHANISH APP
ISLAY	CIV AP	123.15	AFIS (ISLAY INFO)
STRATHALLAN	PRI AF	129.9	AG RADIO
CUMBERNAULD	CIV AF	120.6	AG RADIO / AFIS
GLASGOW	CIV AP	118.8	TWR
		121.7	GRND
		115.4	ATIS (ARR / DEP INFO)
		119.1	APP / RAD
		119.3	RAD
		121.3	RAD
		121.6	FIRE
		132.17	ATIS
		362.3	APP / RAD
GLASGOW CITY HELIPORT	CIV HELIPA	119.1	GLASGOW APP
PRESTWICK	CIV AP	118.15	TWR
		121.8	TWR
		127.12	ATIS
		120.55	APP / RAD
		119.45	RAD
		9013 KHz	RN PRESTWICK HF SSB
		337.75	RN PRESTWICK
WEST FREUGH	MOD AF	122.55	TWR
		130.05	APP / RAD / MATZ
		130.72	RAD
		337.92	TWR
		260.02	APP / RAD
		259.0	RAD / SRE
WIGTON (BALDOON)	PRI AF	123.05	AG RADIO

AREA 3

ZONES & AIRWAYS OF NORTH WEST ENGLAND

FREQUENCY	CALL	SERVICE
119.87	SCOTTISH INFORMATION	EAST
127.27	SCOTTISH INFORMATION	WEST
131.3	SCOTTISH INFORMATION	NORTH
125.72	VOLMET (SCOTTISH)	WEATHER
125.47	LONDON INFORMATION	NORTH
126.6	VOLMET(LONDON NORTH)	WEATHER
135.37	VOLMET (LONDON MAIN)	WEATHER
127.0	VOLMET (DUBLIN)	WEATHER
118.77	LONDON CONTROL	AIRWAYS CONTROL— A1, A2, A20, A25, A47, B1, B3, B4, Y98, Y99
131.05	LONDON CONTROL	AIRWAYS CONTROL— A1, A2, A20, A25, A47, B1, B3, B4, Y98, Y99
126.77	LONDON CONTROL	AIRWAYS CONTROL— A1, A2, A20, A25, A47, B1, B3, B4, Y98, Y99
118.77	LONDON CONTROL	ADVISORY ROUTES— W2D, W911D, W928D
131.05	LONDON CONTROL	ADVISORY ROUTES— W2D, W911D, W928D
126.77	LONDON CONTROL	ADVISORY ROUTES— W2D, W911D, W928D
118.77	LONDON CONTROL	UPPER AIR ROUTES— UA1, UA2, UA34, UR4, UW502, UP6, UL603, UB4, UA25, UY98, UB1
126.77	LONDON CONTROL	UPPER AIR ROUTES— UA1, UA2, UA34, UR4, UW502, UP6, UL603, UB4, UA25, UY98, UB1
131.05	LONDON CONTROL	UPPER AIR ROUTES— UA1, UA2, UA34, UR4, UW502, UP6, UL603, UB4, UA25, UY98, UB1
121.32	LONDON CONTROL	UPPER AIR ROUTES— UA1, UA2, UA34, UR4, UW502, UP6, UL603, UB4, UA25, UY98, UB1
128.12	LONDON CONTROL	UPPER AIR ROUTES— UA1, UA2, UA34, UR4, UW502, UP6, UL603, UB4, UA25, UY98, UB1
133.52	LONDON CONTROL	UPPER AIR ROUTES— UA1, UA2, UA34, UR4, UW502, UP6, UL603, UB4, UA25, UY98, UB1

AREA 3

ZONES & AIRWAYS OF NORTH WEST ENGLAND

FREQUENCY	CALL	SERVICE
231.62	LONDON MILITARY	UPPER MIDDLE & LOWER AIR SPACE SERVICE
127.45	LONDON MILITARY	UPPER MIDDLE & LOWER AIR SPACE SERVICE

AREA 3

AIRFIELDS OF NORTH WEST ENGLAND

STATION	TYPE	FREQUENCY	SERVICE / REMARKS / CALL
SPADEADAM RANGE	MIL RANGE	122.1	AG RADIO
		369.15	AG RADIO
KIRKBRIDE	PRI AF	123.6	CARLISLE APP
CARLISLE	CIV AP	123.6	TWR / APP
BARROW (WALNEY)	PRI AF	123.2	TWR / AG RADIO
CARK	PRI AF	123.45	AG RADIO
BLACKPOOL	CIV AP	118.4	TWR
		121.75	ATIS
		135.95	APP / ATZ
		119.95	RAD / SRE
WARTON	PRI AF	130.8	TWR / APP
		124.45	APP / RAD / MATZ / LARS
		129.72	APP / RAD
		311.3	TWR / APP / RAD
		336.47	APP / RAD / MATZ / LARS
		343.7	RAD / SRE
RONALDSWAY (I O M)	CIV AP	118.9	TWR / APP
		120.85	APP / RAD / LARS
		118.2	RAD
		125.3	RAD
WOODVALE	MIL AF	119.75	TWR
		121.0	APP
		123.5	AG (CLUB FREQ)
		312.8	TWR / APP
		259.95	TWR / APP

AREA 4

ZONES & AIRWAYS OF N. W. ENGLAND & IRISH SEA

FREQUENCY	CALL	SERVICE
127.27	SCOTTISH INFORMATION	WEST
125.72	VOLMET (SCOTTISH)	WEATHER
125.47	LONDON INFORMATION	NORTH
126.6	VOLMET (LONDON NORTH)	WEATHER
135.37	VOLMET (LONDON MAIN)	WEATHER
127.0	VOLMET (DUBLIN)	WEATHER
125.1	MANCHESTER CONTROL	AIRWAYS CONTROL FOR FLIGHTS AT OR BELOW FL195
124.2	MANCHESTER CONTROL	AIRWAYS CONTROL FOR FLIGHTS AT OR BELOW FL195
126.65	MANCHESTER CONTROL	AIRWAYS CONTROL FOR FLIGHTS AT OR BELOW FL195
118.77	LONDON CONTROL	UPPER AIR ROUTES — UA1, UA2, UA25, UA34, UB1, UB3, UB4, UB10, UB39, UL613, UM16, UP6, UR4 UW502
127.1	LONDON CONTROL	UPPER AIR ROUTES — UA1, UA2, UA25, UA34, UB1, UB3, UB4, UB10, UB39, UL613, UM16, UP6, UR4 UW502
131.05	LONDON CONTROL	UPPER AIR ROUTES — UA1, UA2, UA25, UA34, UB1, UB3, UB4, UB10, UB39, UL613, UM16, UP6, UR4 UW502
135.57	LONDON CONTROL	UPPER AIR ROUTES — UA1, UA2, UA25, UA34, UB1, UB3, UB4, UB10, UB39, UL613, UM16, UP6, UR4, UW502
118.77	LONDON CONTROL	AIRWAYS CONTROL — A1, A2, A20, A25, A34, B1, B3, B53, B4, N862, R101, Y99
126.77	LONDON CONTROL	AIRWAYS CONTROL — A1, A2, A20, A25, A34, B1, B3, B53, B4, N862, R101, Y99
131.05	LONDON CONTROL	AIRWAYS CONTROL — A1, A2, A20, A25, A34, B1, B3, B53, B4, N862, R101, Y99
135.57	LONDON CONTROL	AIRWAYS CONTROL — A1, A2, A20, A25, A34, B1, B3, B53, B4, N862, R101, Y99

AREA 4

ZONES & AIRWAYS OF N. W. ENGLAND & IRISH SEA

FREQUENCY	CALL	SERVICE
231.62	LONDON MILITARY	UPPER, MIDDLE & LOWER AIRSPACE SERVICE
127.45	LONDON MILITARY	UPPER, MIDDLE & LOWER AIRSPACE SERVICE

AREA 4

AIRFIELDS OF WEST MIDLANDS & N. WALES

STATION	TYPE	FREQUENCY	SERVICE / REMARKS / CALL
LIVERPOOL	CIV AP	118.1	TWR
		119.85	APP / RAD
		118.45	RAD
HAYDOCK PARK	PRI AF	119.4	MANCHESTER APP
		119.85	LIVERPOOL APP
MANCHESTER (BARTON)	CIV AF	122.7	AG RADIO

NOTE: MANCHESTER SUB CENTRE CONTROLS APPROACH TO MANCHESTER INTERNATIONAL AIRPORT AND AIRWAYS BELOW FLIGHT LEVEL 175 IN ZONE. SEE SECTION ON ZONES & AIRWAYS ABOVE.

STATION	TYPE	FREQUENCY	SERVICE / REMARKS / CALL
MANCHESTER AIRPORT	CIV AP	121.85	INITIAL CALL IN OP HRS
		118.62	TWR
		121.7	CLEARANCE DELIV & GND
		118.57	ARRIVALS
		128.17	ATIS
		119.4	APP / RAD
		121.35	APP RAD
		130.65	EXECUTIVE HANDLING
WOODFORD	PRI AF	126.92	TWR / APP
		130.75	APP
		130.05	RAD
		269.12	TWR / RAD
		358.57	APP / RAD

AREA 4

AIRFIELDS OF WEST MIDLANDS & N. WALES

STATION	TYPE	FREQUENCY	SERVICE / REMARKS / CALL
ASHCROFT	PRI AF	122.52	AG RADIO
CHESTER	CIV AF	124.95	TWR
(HAWARDEN)		123.35	APP
		130.25	RAD
		336.32	TWR
CHETWYND	MIL AF	309.55	TWR (TERNHILL)
		276.07	APP (TERNHILL)
MONA	MIL AF	122.0	AG RADIO / AFIS
		134.35	VALLEY APP / MATZ
		268.77	VALLEY RADAR
		358.75	TWR
		372.32	VALLEY APP
		379.7	APP
VALLEY	MIL AF	122.1	TWR / APP / GRND
		134.35	APP / MATZ / LARS
		123.3	DIRECTOR / PAR RAD
		340.17	TWR
		257.8	TWR
		356.75	GRND
		372.32	APP
		362.3	APP
		337.72	DIR / RAD
		344.0	RAD
		358.67	PAR RADAR
		385.4	PAR RADAR
		252.8	VALLEY RESCUE
CAERNARFON	CIV AF	122.25	AG RADIO
		134.35	VALLEY APP
		122.5	LLANBEDR APP
LLANBEDR	MIL AF	122.5	TWR / APP / PAR RAD
		370.3	PAR
		387.75	TWR
		386.67	APP / PAR RADAR
WELSHPOOL	PRI AF	124.15	SHAWBURY APP
(OAKS FARM)			

AREA 4

AIRFIELDS OF WEST MIDLANDS & N. WALES

STATION	TYPE	FREQUENCY	SERVICE / REMARKS / CALL
WELSHPOOL (TRELIG)	PRI AF	123.25	AG RADIO
TATENHILL	PRI AF	122.2	AG RADIO
WHITCHURCH	PRI AF	130.4	AG RADIO
WHITCHURCH (TISTOCK)	PRI AF	129.9	AG RADIO
MOAT HALL	PRI AF	122.2	AG (TATENHILL RADIO)
SHAWBURY	MIL AF	122.1	TWR
		120.77	APP / RAD / MATZ / LARS
		123.3	PAR RADAR
		340.35	TWR
		257.8	TWR
		337.9	GRND
		362.47	APP
		362.3	APP
		356.97	PAR RADAR
		385.4	PAR RADAR
TERNHILL	MIL AF	120.77	TWR / APP / MATZ
		122.1	APP
		338.82	TWR
		309.55	CHETWYND TRAFFIC
		276.82	APP
		356.32	APP
		362.3	APP
SLEAP	CIV AF	122.45	AG RADIO
		124.15	SHAWBURY APP
LEDBURY (VELCOURT)	PRI AF	125.65	GLOUCESTER APP
HALFPENNY GREEN	CIV AF	123.0	AG RADIO / AFIS
SHOBDEN	CIV AF	123.5	AG RADIO
COSFORD	MIL AF	118.92	APP/TWR
		357.12	TWR
		276.12	APP
		121.95	GND

AREA 5 & 8

ZONES & AIRWAYS OF THE EAST & WEST MIDLANDS

FREQUENCY	CALL	SERVICE
125.47	LONDON INFORMATION	NORTH
124.75	LONDON INFORMATION	SOUTH WEST
126.6	VOLMET (LONDON NORTH)	WEATHER
135.57	VOLMET (LONDON MAIN)	WEATHER
118.47	LONDON CONTROL	AIRWAYS CONTROL — A1, A2, A20, A34, A47, B3, B4, B71, B317, B321, R41, W70
127.1	LONDON CONTROL	AIRWAYS CONTROL — A1, A2, A20, A34, A47, B3, B4, B71, B317, B321, R41, W70
128.42	LONDON CONTROL	AIRWAYS CONTROL — A1, A2, A20, A34, A47, B3, B4, B71, B317, B321, R41, W70
130.92	LONDON CONTROL	AIRWAYS CONTROL — A1, A2, A20, A34, A47, B3, B4, B71, B317, B321, R41, W70
131.12	LONDON CONTROL	AIRWAYS CONTROL — A1, A2, A20, A34, A47, B3, B4, B71, B317, B321, R41, W70
132.45	LONDON CONTROL	AIRWAYS CONTROL — A1, A2, A20, A34, A47, B3, B4, B71, B317, B321, R41, W70
118.47	LONDON CONTROL	UPPER AIR ROUTES — UA1, UA34, UB3, UB39, UB71, UB317, UB321, UR41, UY98
127.1	LONDON CONTROL	UPPER AIR ROUTES — UA1, UA34, UB3, UB39, UB71, UB317, UB321, UR41, UY98
127.87	LONDON CONTROL	UPPER AIR ROUTES — UA1, UA34, UB3, UB39, UB71, UB317, UB321, UR41, UY98
128.47	LONDON CONTROL	UPPER AIR ROUTES — UA1, UA34, UB3, UB39, UB71, UB317, UB321, UR41, UY98
130.92	LONDON CONTROL	UPPER AIR ROUTES — UA1, UA34, UB3, UB39, UB71, UB317, UB321, UR41, UY98

AREA 5 & 8

ZONES & AIRWAYS OF THE EAST & WEST MIDLANDS

FREQUENCY	CALL	SERVICE
131.12	LONDON CONTROL	UPPER AIR ROUTES — UA1, UA34, UB3, UB39, UB71, UB317, UB321, UR41, UY98
132.45	LONDON CONTROL	UPPER AIR ROUTES — UA1, UA34, UB3, UB39, UB71, UB317, UB321, UR41, UY98
127.45	LONDON MILITARY	UPPER, MIDDLE & LOWER AIRSPACE SERVICE
135.15	LONDON MILITARY	UPPER, MIDDLE & LOWER AIRSPACE SERVICE
231.62	LONDON MILITARY	UPPER, MIDDLE & LOWER AIRSPACE SERVICE
275.47	LONDON MILITARY	UPPER, MIDDLE & LOWER AIRSPACE SERVICE
257.1	BRIZE RADAR	MIDDLE & LOWER AIRSPACE SERVICE
134.3	BRIZE RADAR	MIDDLE & LOWER AIRSPACE SERVICE

AREA 5

AIRFIELDS OF THE MIDLANDS & THAMES VALLEY

STATION	TYPE	FREQUENCY	SERVICE / REMARKS / CALL
BIRMINGHAM	CIV AP	118.3	TWR
		121.8	GRND
		126.27	ATIS
		131.32	ATC
		118.05	APP / RAD
		131.85	EXECUTIVE OPS
COVENTRY	CIV AP	124.8	TWR / GRND
		121.7	GRND
		119.25	TWR / APP / RAD
		126.05	ATIS
		122.0	RAD / SRE

AREA 5

AIRFIELDS OF THE MIDLANDS & THAMES VALLEY

STATION	TYPE	FREQUENCY	SERVICE / REMARKS / CALL
WELLSBOURNE MOUNTFORD	CIV AF	124.02	AG RADIO
NORTHAMPTON (SYWELL)	CIV AF	122.7	AG RADIO / AFIS
WESTON ON THE GREEN	MIL AF	133.65	TWR CALL RAF
		134.3	TWR CALL RAF
		257.1	BRIZE RADAR
CROUGHTON	MIL USAF	17.976 KHz	AG RADIO (SSB)
		15.016 KHz	AG RADIO (SSB)
		13.200 KHz	AG RADIO (SSB)
		11.175 KHz	AG RADIO (SSB)
		8.992 KHz	AG RADIO (SSB)
		6.712 KHz	AG RADIO (SSB)
		4.724 KHz	AG RADIO (SSB)
		343.6	AG RADIO
HINTON-IN-THE-HEDGES	PRI AF	119.45	AIR TO AIR
ENSTONE	CIV AF	129.87	AG RADIO
TURWESTON	PRI AF	122.17	AG RADIO
SILVERSTONE	PRI AF	121.07	TWR / AG
CHALGROVE	PRI AF	125.4	AG RADIO
OXFORD (KIDLINGTON)	CIV AF	118.87	TWR / AG RADIO / AFIS
		121.95	GRND
		121.75	ATIS
		125.32	APP
		134.3	BRIZE RADAR
REDLANDS	PRI AF	129.82	AG RADIO
ABINGDON (SEE BENSON)	MIL AF	134.3	BRIZE RADAR
BENSON	MIL AF	130.25	TWR
		122.1	TWR / APP / DIR
		120.9	APP / RAD / MATZ
		127.15	APP
		123.3	DIRECTOR / SRE
		134.3	BRIZE RADAR
		279.35	TWR
		340.32	GRND

AREA 5

AIRFIELDS OF THE MIDLANDS & THAMES VALLEY

STATION	TYPE	FREQUENCY	SERVICE / REMARKS / CALL
BENSON (continued)		268.82	APP
		344.0	APP / DIR
		315.75	DIR /SRE
		358.8	BENSON ZONE
		362.3	BENSON ZONE
		259.87	PAR
		241.62	PAR
		257.1	BRIZE RADAR

AMENDMENTS

STATION	TYPE	FREQUENCY	SERVICE / REMARKS / CALL

AREA 5A

ZONES & AIRWAYS OF SOUTH MIDLANDS & SOUTH WALES

FREQUENCY	CALL	SERVICE
124.75	LONDON INFORMATION	SOUTH WEST
124.6	LONDON INFORMATION	SOUTH EAST
135.57	VOLMET (LONDON MAIN)	WEATHER
128.6	VOLMET (LONDON SOUTH)	WEATHER
127.1	LONDON CONTROL	AIRWAYS CONTROL — A1, A2, A20, A25, A34, A47, B3, B4, B39, B71, B317, B321, G1, R41, W70, Y3
129.1	LONDON CONTROL	AIRWAYS CONTROL — A1, A2, A20, A25, A34, A47, B3, B4, B39, B71, B317, B321, G1, R41, W70, Y3
129.37	LONDON CONTROL	AIRWAYS CONTROL — A1, A2, A20, A25, A34, A47, B3, B4, B39, B71, B317, B321, G1, R41, W70, Y3
130.92	LONDON CONTROL	AIRWAYS CONTROL — A1, A2, A20, A25, A34, A47, B3, B4, B39, B71, B317, B321, G1, R41, W70, Y3
131.05	LONDON CONTROL	AIRWAYS CONTROL — A1, A2, A20, A25, A34, A47, B3, B4, B39, B71, B317, B321, G1, R41, W70, Y3
131.12	LONDON CONTROL	AIRWAYS CONTROL — A1, A2, A20, A25, A34, A47, B3, B4, B39, B71, B317, B321, G1, R41, W70, Y3
132.45	LONDON CONTROL	AIRWAYS CONTROL — A1, A2, A20, A25, A34, A47, B3, B4, B39, B71, B317, B321, G1, R41, W70, Y3
132.6	LONDON CONTROL	AIRWAYS CONTROL — A1, A2, A20, A25, A34, A47, B3, B4, B39, B71, B317, B321, G1, R41, W70, Y3
133.6	LONDON CONTROL	AIRWAYS CONTROL — A1, A2, A20, A25, A34, A47, B3, B4, B39, B71, B317, B321, G1, R41, W70, Y3
134.75	LONDON CONTROL	AIRWAYS CONTROL — A1, A2, A20, A25, A34, A47, B3, B4, B39, B71, B317, B321, G1, R41, W70, Y3
127.1	LONDON CONTROL	UPPER AIR ROUTES — UA1, UA25, UA29, UA34, UB3, UB39, UB40, UB71, UB317, UB321, UG1, UL607, UN546, UN862, UP2, UP4, UR14, UR41, UW502, UY98

AREA 5A

ZONES & AIRWAYS OF SOUTH MIDLANDS & SOUTH WALES

FREQUENCY	CALL	SERVICE
129.1	LONDON CONTROL	UPPER AIR ROUTES — UA1, UA25, UA29, UA34, UB3, UB39, UB40, UB71, UB317, UB321, UG1, UL607, UN546, UN862, UP2, UP4, UR14, UR41, UW502, UY98
129.37	LONDON CONTROL	UPPER AIR ROUTES — UA1, UA25, UA29, UA34, UB3, UB39, UB40, UB71, UB317, UB321, UG1, UL607, UN546, UN862, UP2, UP4, UR14, UR41, UW502, UY98
130.92	LONDON CONTROL	UPPER AIR ROUTES — UA1, UA25, UA29, UA34, UB3, UB39, UB40, UB71, UB317, UB321, UG1, UL607, UN546, UN862, UP2, UP4, UR14, UR41, UW502, UY98
131.05	LONDON CONTROL	UPPER AIR ROUTES — UA1, UA25, UA29, UA34, UB3, UB39, UB40, UB71, UB317, UB321, UG1, UL607, UN546, UN862, UP2, UP4, UR14, UR41, UW502, UY98
131.12	LONDON CONTROL	UPPER AIR ROUTES — UA1, UA25, UA29, UA34, UB3, UB39, UB40, UB71, UB317, UB321, UG1, UL607, UN546, UN862, UP2, UP4, UR14, UR41, UW502, UY98
132.45	LONDON CONTROL	UPPER AIR ROUTES — UA1, UA25, UA29, UA34, UB3, UB39, UB40, UB71, UB317, UB321, UG1, UL607, UN546, UN862, UP2, UP4, UR14, UR41, UW502, UY98
132.6	LONDON CONTROL	UPPER AIR ROUTES — UA1, UA25, UA29, UA34, UB3, UB39, UB40, UB71, UB317, UB321, UG1, UL607, UN546, UN862, UP2, UP4, UR14, UR41, UW502, UY98

AREA 5A

ZONES & AIRWAYS OF SOUTH MIDLANDS & SOUTH WALES

FREQUENCY	CALL	SERVICE
133.6	LONDON CONTROL	UPPER AIR ROUTES — UA1, UA25, UA29, UA34, UB3, UB39, UB40, UB71, UB317, UB321, UG1, UL607, UN546, UN862, UP2, UP4, UR14, UR41, UW502, UY98
134.75	LONDON CONTROL	UPPER AIR ROUTES — UA1, UA25, UA29, UA34, UB3, UB39, UB40, UB71, UB317, UB321, UG1, UL607, UN546, UN862, UP2, UP4, UR14, UR41, UW502, UY98
136.4	LONDON CONTROL	UPPER AIR ROUTES — UA1, UA25, UA29, UA34, UB3, UB39, UB40, UB71, UB317, UB321, UG1, UL607, UN546, UP2, UP4, UR14, UR41, UW502, UY98
127.45	LONDON MILITARY	UPPER, MIDDLE & LOWER AIRSPACE SERVICE
135.15	LONDON MILITARY	UPPER, MIDDLE & LOWER AIRSPACE SERVICE
231.62	LONDON MILITARY	UPPER, MIDDLE & LOWER AIRSPACE SERVICE
275.47	LONDON MILITARY	UPPER, MIDDLE & LOWER AIRSPACE SERVICE
257.1	BRIZE RADAR	MIDDLE & LOWER AIRSPACE SERVICE
134.3	BRIZE RADAR	MIDDLE & LOWER AIRSPACE SERVICE

AREA 5A

AIRFIELDS OF THE UPPER THAMES VALLEY & SOUTH WALES

STATION	TYPE	FREQUENCY	SERVICE / REMARKS / CALL
NEWBURY RACECOURSE	PRI AF	134.3	BRIZE RADAR
		126.7	BOSCOMBE APP
BRIZE NORTON	MIL AF	126.5	TWR / GRND
		133.75	DIR / APP
		130.07	OPS
		119.0	DIR / SRE / MATZ / LARS
		134.3	BRIZE RADAR / LARS
		123.3	PAR / SRE
		396.7	TWR
		257.8	TWR
		370.3	GRND
		126.5	GRND
		254.47	ATIS
		357.47	OPS
		342.45	APP
		362.3	APP
		257.1	BRIZE RAD / LARS/MARS
		356.87	DIR / APP / RAD
		344.0	DIR / APP / RAD
		338.65	PAR RAD
		385.4	PAR RAD
WROUGHTON	MIL AF	133.65	TWR
		123.22	AG RADIO
		315.1	TWR
DRAYCOTT	PRI AF	118.42	LYNEHAM APP
LYNEHAM	MIL AF	119.22	TWR
		122.1	TWR
		118.42	TWR / GRND / APP
		123.4	DIRECTOR / APP / RAD
		134.3	BRIZE RADAR
		123.3	PAR RADAR
		386.82	TWR
		129.47	GRND
		340.17	GRND
		254.65	OPS
		345.02	SRE
		277.92	ATIS
		359.5	APP
		362.3	APP

AIRFIELDS OF THE UPPER THAMES VALLEY & SOUTH WALES

STATION	TYPE	FREQUENCY	SERVICE / REMARKS / CALL
LYNEHAM (continued)		300.47	DIR
		344.00	DIR
		375.2	PAR RADAR
		385.4	PAR RADAR
OAKSEY PARK	PRI AF	122.77	AG RADIO
		123.4	LYNHAM APP
FAIRFORD	MIL USAF	142.22	TWR
		122.1	TWR / APP /BRIZE RADAR
		119.0	BRIZE DIR / MATZ
		134.3	MATZ /BRIZE RADAR
		337.57	TWR
		119.15	TWR
		342.45	APP
		362.3	APP
		259.97	GRND
		379.47	DISPATCHER
		307.8	COMMAND POST
		371.2	COMMAND POST
		358.6	FAIRFORD METRO
		376.62	BRIZE RADAR / MATZ
		257.1	BRIZE RADAR
BADMINTON	PRI AF	123.17	AG RADIO
		123.4	LYNEHAM APP
		122.72	FILTON APP
GLOUCESTERSHIRE	CIV AP	122.9	TWR
		127.47	ATIS
		125.65	APP
		120.97	RAD
FILTON (BRISTOL)	PRI AF	132.35	TWR
		122.72	APP / RAD / LARS
		127.97	RAD
		342.02	TWR
		256.12	APP / RAD / LARS
		336.47	DIR
BRISTOL	CIV AP	133.85	TWR
		126.02	ATIS
		128.55	APP
		124.35	RAD

AREA 5A

AIRFIELDS OF THE SEVERN VALLEY & SOUTH WALES

STATION	TYPE	FREQUENCY	SERVICE / REMARKS / CALL
WESTBURY-SUB-MENDIP	PRI AF	132.4	BRISTOL APP
		127.35	YEOVILTON APP
WESTON-SUPER-MARE	PRI AF	122.5	TWR
		129.25	APP
CARDIFF	CIV AP	125.0	TWR
		119.47	ATIS
		125.85	APP / RAD / LARS
		124.1	PAR RADAR
		277.22	APP / RAD
ST ATHAN	MIL AF	122.1	TWR / APP
		119.47	ATIS CARDIFF INFO
		125.85	CARDIFF APP
		123.3	RAD / DIRECTOR
		336.52	TWR
		257.8	TWR
		277.22	CARDIFF APP
		357.17	APP
		362.3	APP
		386.5	GND
TREMORFA HELIPORT	CIV PAD	129.9	AG RADIO
		125.85	CARDIFF APP
SWANSEA	CIV AF	119.7	TWR / APP
BRAWDY	MIL AF	122.4	AG / BRAWDY RESCUE
		123.1	SAR
HAVERFORD WEST	CIV AF	122.2	AG RADIO
		124.4	BRAWDY RESCUE
MANORBIER	MIL RANGE	336.22	AG RADIO
		360.77	AG RADIO
ABERPORTH	MIL AF	122.15	AFIS
		259.0	TWR

NORTH SEA OIL RIGS

The following frequencies are currently in use for services to/from North Sea oil rigs

120.07,	122.0,	122.02,	122.12,	122.37,	122.62,
122.65,	122.87,	122.95,	123.02,	123.45,	123.62,
123.65,	125.17,	129.7,	129.87,	129.9,	130.55,
130.87,	133.57,	133.87			

AREA 6

ZONES & AIRWAYS OF THE NORTH EAST OF ENGLAND

FREQUENCY	CALL	SERVICE
125.47	LONDON INFORMATION	NORTH
119.87	SCOTTISH INFORMATION	SCOTTISH
126.6	VOLMET (LONDON NORTH)	WEATHER
299.97	LONDON MILITARY	
135.27	LONDON MILITARY	
231.62	LONDON MILITARY	
125.27	ANGLIA RADAR	ADVISORY & INFORMATION SERVICE
128.92	ANGLIA RADAR	ADVISORY & INFORMATION SERVICE
283.47	ANGLIA RADAR	ADVISORY & INFORMATION SERVICE
126.77	LONDON CONTROL	AIRWAYS CONTROL — B1, L602
128.12	LONDON CONTROL	AIRWAYS CONTROL — B1, L602
121.32	LONDON CONTROL	AIRWAYS CONTROL — B1, L602

NOTE: SEVERAL ROUTES IN THIS AREA DO NOT HAVE IDENTITIES

118.77	LONDON CONTROL	UPPER AIR ROUTES — UA37, UB1, UL74, UR4, UR38, UR532, UN591, UW534, UW536, UW538, UW550
131.05	LONDON CONTROL	UPPER AIR ROUTES — UA37, UB1, UL74, UR4, UR38, UR532, UN591, UW534, UW536, UW538, UW550
126.77	LONDON CONTROL	UPPER AIR ROUTES — UA37, UB1, UL74, UR4, UR38, UR532, UN591, UW534, UW536, UW538, UW550

AREA 6

ZONES & AIRWAYS OF THE NORTH EAST OF ENGLAND

FREQUENCY	CALL	SERVICE
128.12	LONDON CONTROL	UPPER AIR ROUTES — UA37, UB1, UL74, UR4, UR38, UR532, UN591, UW534, UW536, UW538, UW550
121.32	LONDON CONTROL	UPPER AIR ROUTES — UA37, UB1, UL74, UR4, UR38, UR532, UN591, UW534, UW536, UW538, UW550
128.67	PENNINE RADAR	ADVISORY ROUTE — W911D, ALSO DIRECT TRACKS

AREA 6

AIRFIELDS OF THE NORTH EASTERN COUNTIES

STATION	TYPE	FREQUENCY	SERVICE / REMARKS / CALL
CHARTERHALL	PRI AF	119.87	SCOTTISH INFORMATION
WINFIELD	PRI AF	123.5	AG RADIO
BOULMER	MIL AF	123.1	AG RADIO
		282.8	SAR
		299.1	AG
ESHOTT	PRI AF	134.7	LONDON INFORMATION
		124.37	NEWCASTLE APP
NEWCASTLE INTERNATIONAL	CIV AP	119.7	TWR
		114.25	ATIS
		118.5	APP / RAD
		124.37	APP / LARS / RAD
		284.6	APP / RAD / LARS
FISHBURN (MORGANFIELD)	PRI AF	118.85	TEES-SIDE APP
TEES-SIDE	CIV AP	119.8	TWR
		118.85	APP / RAD
		128.85	RAD
		379.8	TWR
		296.72	APP / RAD

AREA 6

AIRFIELDS OF THE NORTH EASTERN COUNTIES

STATION	TYPE	FREQUENCY	SERVICE / REMARKS / CALL
LEEMING	MIL AF	120.5	TWR
		122.1	TWR
		132.4	TWR
		123.3	APP / RAD
		127.75	APP / MATZ / LARS
		344.57	TWR
		257.8	TWR
		249.52	AFIS
		386.52	GRND
		356.72	OPS
		358.65	DIR
		344.0	DIR
		362.3	APP
		292.7	RAD / LARS
		336.35	PAR RADAR
		309.87	PAR RADAR
		385.4	PAR RADAR
DISHFORTH	MIL AF	122.1	TWR / GRND
		130.1	AG RADIO
		125.0	TOPCLIFFE APP
		357.37	APP
		362.3	APP
		379.67	GRND
		259.82	TWR
		252.9	OPS
BAGBY (THIRSK)	PRI AF	123.25	AG RADIO
		127.75	LEEMING APP
SUTTON BANK	CIV AF	130.4	AG (GLIDER FREQ)
MARSTON MOOR	CIV AF	122.97	AG RADIO
		129.5	LINTON APP
POCKLINGTON	PRI AF	130.1	AG RADIO
FADMOOR	PRI AF	123.22	AG RADIO
WILLY HOWE	PRI AG	130.12	AG RADIO
BRIDLINGTON (CARNABY)	CIV AF	123.25	AG RADIO
BERVERLEY	PRI AF	123.05	AG RADIO

AREA 6

AIRFIELDS OF THE NORTH EASTERN COUNTIES

STATION	TYPE	FREQUENCY	SERVICE / REMARKS / CALL
LECONFIELD	MIL AF	123.05	SAR
		244.87	SAR
		282.8	SAR
BREIGHTON	PRI AF	129.8	AG RADIO
LINTON ON-OUSE	MIL AF	122.1	TWR
		129.15	AG / APP / MATZ / LARS
		123.3	PAR RADAR
		300.42	TWR
		257.8	TWR
		344.47	SRE
		277.62	DEPS
		340.02	GRND
		362.67	APP
		362.3	APP
		292.8	DIR /LARS
		344.0	DIR
		358.52	PAR RADAR
		259.87	PAR RADAR
RUFFORTH	CIV AF	130.4	AF RADIO
		129.97	AG GLIDERS ONLY
TOPCLIFFE	MIL AF	130.82	TWR
		122.1	TWR / APP
		125.0	APP
		123.3	PAR RADAR
		255.6	SRE
		344.0	SRE
		309.72	TWR
		257.8	TWR
		357.37	APP
		362.3	APP
		387.45	GRND
		344.35	DIR / PAR RADAR
		385.4	DIR / PAR RADAR
ELVINGTON	MIL AF	126.5	FENTON APP / MATZ
		352.4	TWR
		371.4	APP
YORK (ACASTER MALBIS)	PRI AF	126.5	FENTON APP
		129.15	LINTON ZONE

AREA 6

AIRFIELDS OF THE NORTH EASTERN COUNTIES

STATION	TYPE	FREQUENCY	SERVICE / REMARKS / CALL
POCKLINGTON	PRI AF	130.1	AG RADIO
CHURCH FENTON	MIL AF	122.1	TWR / GRND
		126.5	APP
		254.52	APP
		123.3	PAR RADAR
		262.7	TWR
		257.8	TWR
		375.32	SRE
		340.2	GRND
		362.3	APP
		344.0	DIR
		386.72	PAR RADAR
		385.4	PAR RADAR
SHERBURN IN ELMET	CIV AF	122.6	AG RADIO
		129.15	LINTON APP
PAULL (HULL)	PRI AF	123.0	AG RADIO
HULL (BURTON CONSTABLE)	PRI AF	122.75	COWDEN RANGE
BROUGH	PRI AF	130.55	TWR / AG RADIO
		310.35	TWR
		379.77	RAD
LEEDS / BRADFORD	CIV AP	120.3	TWR
		118.02	ATIS
		123.75	APP / VDF
		121.05	RAD
HUDDERSFIELD	CIV AF	122.2	AG RADIO

AREA 7 AND 8A

ZONES & AIRWAYS OF HUMBERSIDE & EAST MIDLANDS

FREQUENCY	CALL	SERVICE
125.47	LONDON INFORMATION	NORTH
124.6	LONDON INFORMATION	EAST
128.6	VOLMET (LONDON SOUTH)	WEATHER
135.37	VOLMET (LONDON MAIN)	WEATHER
125.27	ANGLIA RADAR	ADVISORY & INFORMATION SERVICE
128.92	ANGLIA RADAR	ADVISORY & INFORMATION SERVICE
283.47	ANGLIA RADAR	ADVISORY & INFORMATION SERVICE
264.57	ANGLIA RADAR	ADVISORY & INFORMATION SERVICE
118.47	LONDON CONTROL	AIRWAYS CONTROL — A2, A20, A37, B3, B4, B29, B317, H52, H53, H54, R1, R12, R77, R123, R126
129.6	LONDON CONTROL	AIRWAYS CONTROL — A2, A20, A37, B3, B4, B29, B317, H52, H53, H54, R1, R12, R77, R123, R126
132.6	LONDON CONTROL	AIRWAYS CONTROL — A2, A20, A37, B3, B4, B29, B317, H52, H53, H54, R1, R12, R77, R123, R126
135.45	LONDON CONTROL	AIRWAYS CONTROL — A2, A20, A37, B3, B4, B29, B317, H52, H53, H54, R1, R12, R77, R123, R126
133.45	LONDON CONTROL	AIRWAYS CONTROL — A2, A20, A37, B3, B4, B29, B317, H52, H53, H54, R1, R12, R77, R123, R126
118.47	LONDON CONTROL	UPPER AIR ROUTES — UA2, UA37, UB4, UB29, UB39, UB71, UB317, UB295, UH53, UH54, UL608, UL603, UL613, UM14, UR12, UR77, UR123, UR126, UW501, UW550
129.6	LONDON CONTROL	UPPER AIR ROUTES — UA2, UA37, UB4, UB29, UB39, UB71, UB317, UB295, UH53, UH54, UL608, UL603, UL613, UM14, UR12, UR77, UR123, UR126, UW501, UW550

AREA 7 AND 8A

ZONES & AIRWAYS OF HUMBERSIDE & EAST MIDLANDS

FREQUENCY	CALL	SERVICE
126.77	LONDON CONTROL	UPPER AIR ROUTES — UA2, UA37, UB4, UB29, UB39, UB71, UB317, UB295, UH53, UH54, UL608, UL603, UL613, UM14, UR12, UR77, UR123, UR126, UW501, UW550
128.12	LONDON CONTROL	UPPER AIR ROUTES — UA2, UA37, UB4, UB29, UB39, UB71, UB317, UB295, UH53, UH54, UL608, UL603, UL613, UM14, UR12, UR77, UR123, UR126, UW501, UW550
132.45	LONDON CONTROL	UPPER AIR ROUTES — UA2, UA37, UB4, UB29, UB39, UB71, UB317, UB295, UH53, UH54, UL608, UL603, UL613, UM14, UR12, UR77, UR123, UR126, UW501, UW550
133.45	LONDON CONTROL	UPPER AIR ROUTES — UA2, UA37, UB4, UB29, UB39, UB71, UB317, UB295, UH53, UH54, UL608, UL603, UL613, UM14, UR12, UR77, UR123, UR126, UW501, UW550
135.42	LONDON CONTROL	UPPER LONDON (WEST)
134.45	LONDON CONTROL	UPPER LONDON (EAST)
291.07	LONDON MILITARY	(HIGH LEVEL OVER FLIGHTS)
275.35	LONDON MILITARY	UPPER, MIDDLE & LOWER AIRSPACE SERVICE
299.97	LONDON MILITARY	UPPER, MIDDLE & LOWER AIRSPACE SERVICE
135.27	LONDON MILITARY	UPPER, MIDDLE & LOWER AIRSPACE SERVICE

AREA 7

AIRFIELDS OF HUMBERSIDE, E. MIDLANDS & LINCS.

STATION	TYPE	FREQUENCY	SERVICE / REMARKS / CALL
HUMBERSIDE INTL	CIV AP	118.55	TWR
		124.67	TWR / APP
		124.12	ATIS
		123.15	RAD
GRIMSBY (CUXWOLD)	PRI AF	122.35	AG RADIO
DONNA NOOK	MIL RANGE	123.05	AG RADIO
DONCASTER	CIV AF	AG RADIO	
		120.35	FINNINGLEY APP
SANDTOFT	CIV AF	130.42	AG RADIO
		120.35	FINNINGLEY RAD / MATZ
COWICK HALL	PRI AF	130.65	AG RADIO
GAMSTON (RETFORD)	CIV AF	130.47	AG RADIO
STURGATE	CIV AF	130.3	AG RADIO
		127.35	WADDINGTON APP
WICKENBY	CIV AF	122.45	AG RADIO
		127.35	WADDINGTON APP
CONINGSBY	MIL AF	119.97	TWR / APP / GRND
		122.1	TWR / APP / GRND
		120.8	APP / GRND / MATZ
		123.3	PAR RADAR
		275.87	TWR
		358.55	GRND
		312.22	APP / MATZ
		362.3	APP
		344.62	APP
		262.95	DIR
		344.0	DIR
		300.92	PAR RADAR
		337.97	PAR RADAR
WADDINGTON	MIL AF	127.35	APP / MATZ / LARS
		123.3	DIR / DEPARTURES
		125.35	RAD / SRE
		388.22	TWR
		257.8	TWR
		342.12	GRND
		244.27	OPS
		312.5	APP / RAD
		291.67	ATIS
		362.3	APP

AREA 7

AIRFIELDS OF HUMBERSIDE, E. MIDLANDS & LINCS.

STATION	TYPE	FREQUENCY	SERVICE / REMARKS / CALL
WADDINGTON		300.57	DIR
(continued)		249.85	DEPARTURES
		344.0	DIR
		296.75	RAD / LARS
		309.67	PAR RADAR
		385.4	PAR RADAR
TEMPLE BRUER	PRI AF	119.0	CRANWELL APP
		127.35	WADDINGTON APP
CRANWELL	MIL AF	119.37	APP
		122.1	TWR / APP
		119.0	APP / MATZ
		123.3	DIR / PAR RADAR
		379.52	TWR
		257.8	TWR
		297.9	GRND
		340.47	APP
		362.3	APP
		250.05	ZONE
		282.0	DIR
		344.0	DIR
		247.17	ATIS
		356.92	PAR RADAR
		285.15	PAR RADAR
CRANWELL NORTH	MIL AF	———	GLIDER OPS ONLY
BARKSTON HEATH	MIL AF	119.0	MATZ
		342.07	TWR
		340.47	CRANWELL APP
NOTTINGHAM	CIV AF	122.8	AG RADIO
		119.65	EAST MIDLANDS APP
COAL ASTON	PRI AF	124.6	LONDON INFORMATION
NETHERTHORPE	CIV AF	123.27	AG RADIO / AFIS
HUCKNALL	PRI AF	130.8	AG RADIO
EAST MIDLANDS	CIV AP	124.0	TWR / RAD / SRE
		121.9	GRND
		128.22	ATIS
		119.65	APP
		120.12	RAD / SRE

AREA 7

AIRFIELDS OF HUMBERSIDE, E. MIDLANDS & LINCS.

STATION	TYPE	FREQUENCY	SERVICE / REMARKS / CALL
DERBY	CIV AF	118.35	AG RADIO
		119.65	EAST MIDLANDS APP
NEWTON	MIL AF	122.1	TWR / APP
		375.42	TWR
		257.8	TWR
		251.72	APP
		362.3	RAD
LEICESTER	CIV AF	122.12	AG RADIO
LANGAR	PRI AF	129.9	LANGAR DZ
		130.2	COTTESMORE APP
SPANHOE	PRI AF	130.2	COTTISMORE APP
		122.1	WITTERING TWR
COTTESMORE	MIL AF	122.1	TWR / GRND
		123.3	WITTERING APP
		130.2	TWR / APP / MATZ / LARS
		370.05	TWR
		257.8	TWR
		312.07	DIR / APP
		340.57	APP / LARS
		388.52	WITTERING APP
		376.57	DEPARTURE CONTROL
		358.72	DIR / MATZ
		336.37	GRND
		262.9	PAR RADAR
		337.87	PAR RADAR
STRUBBY	PRI AF	122.37	AG RADIO
		130.1	GLIDERS
		3453 kHZ	SSB RADIO
SKEGNESS (INGOLDMELLS)	CIV AF	130.45	AG RADIO

AREA 8
AIRFIELDS OF THE COUNTIES NORTH OF LONDON

STATION	TYPE	FREQUENCY	SERVICE / REMARKS / CALL
FENLAND	CIV AF	122.92	AG RADIO. AFIS
LEICESTER	CIV AF	122.12	AG RADIO
BRUNTINGTHORPE	CIV AF	122.82	AG RADIO
CROWLAND	PRI AF	130.2	COTTISMORE APP
WITTERING	MIL AF	122.1	TWR
		388.52	TWR / APP
		130.2	APP / MATZ
		123.3	PAR RADAR
		357.15	TWR
		257.8	TWR
		311.95	GRND
		362.3	BASE APP
		376.57	DEPARTURE CONTROL
		344.0	DEPARTURE CONTROL
		396.85	PAR RADAR
		337.95	PAR RADAR
LITTLE GRANSDEN	CIV AF	130.85	AG RADIO
DEENETHORPE	CIV AF	127.57	AG RADIO
		130.20	COTTISMORE APP
NORTHAMPTON (SYWELL)	CIV AF	122.7	AG RADIO
SIBSON	CIV AF	122.3	AG RADIO
CONNINGTON	CIV AF	129.72	AG RADIO
		134.05	WYTON APP
MARHAM	MIL AF	122.1	TWR
		124.15	APP / RAD / MATZ / LARS
		123.3	PAR RADAR
		337.9	TWR
		257.8	TWR
		336.35	GRND
		261.2	ATIS
		312.55	OPS
		268.87	APP / LARS
		362.3	APP
		293.77	RAD
		344.0	RAD
		379.65	PAR RADAR
		385.4	PAR RADAR

AREA 8

AIRFIELDS OF THE COUNTIES NORTH OF LONDON

STATION	TYPE	FREQUENCY	SERVICE / REMARKS / CALL
BOUGHTON	PRI AF	124.15	MARHAM APP
CAMBRIDGE	CIV AF	122.2	TWR
		123.6	APP
		130.75	RAD / SRE
		372.42	TWR / RAD
BOURN	PRI AF	129.8	AG RADIO
FOWLMERE	CIV AF	120.92	AG RADIO
		125.55	STANSTED APP
		122.07	DUXFORD INFO
OLD WARDEN	PRI AF	123.05	AG ON DISPLAY DAYS
CRANFIELD	PRI AF	134.92	TWR
		121.87	ATIS
		122.85	TWR / APP / RAD
DUXFORD	PRI AF	122.07	AG RADIO
DUNSTABLE	PRI AF	129.55	LUTON APP
LUTON	CIV AP	132.55	TWR
		121.75	GRND
		120.57	ATIS. ARR / DEP INFO
		129.55	APP / LARS
		126.72	APP / RAD
		128.75	APP
LONDON STANSTED	CIV AP	123.8	TWR
		121.72	GRND
		127.17	ATIS. ARR / DEP INFO
		126.95	RAD
		120.62	APP
		125.55	APP / RAD
HIGH EASTER	PRI AF	125.55	STANSTED APP

AREA 8A

AIRFIELDS OF ANGLIA & COUNTIES N.E. OF LONDON

STATION	TYPE	FREQUENCY	SERVICE / REMARKS / CALL
GREAT MASSINGHAM	PRI AF	124.15	MARHAM APP
SHIPDHAM	CIV AF	119.55	AG RADIO
LITTLE SNORING	CIV AF	124.15	MARHAM APP
CROMER	PRI AF	129.82	AG RADIO
COLTISHALL	MIL AF	142.29	TWR
		122.1	TWR / APP
		125.9	APP / MATZ / LARS
		123.3	SRE
		339.95	TWR
		296.72	GRND
		364.8	OPS
		315.32	APP / MATZ
		342.25	DIR / APP
		293.42	DIR / APP / LARS
		275.97	PAR RADAR
		254.25	PAR RADAR
LUDHAM	CIV AF	119.35	NORWICH APP
BACTON	CIV AF	123.45	AG RADIO
FELTHORPE	PRI AF	123.5	AG RADIO
NORWICH	CIV AP	124.25	TWR
		119.35	APP / RAD
		128.32	RAD / SRE
NORTH DENES **(GREAT YARMOUTH)**	CIV AF	123.4	TWR / APP
		3453 KHz	(SSB TRANSMISSIONS)
		5645 KHz	(SSB TRANSMISSIONS)
SOUTH BURLINGHAM	PRI AF	119.35	NORWICH APP
		125.9	COLTISHALL APP
SWANTON MORELY	MIL AF	123.5	AG RADIO
BECCLES	CIV AF	134.6	AG RADIO
FOULSHAM	PRI AF	130.65	AG RADIO
HETHEL	PRI AF	122.35	AG RADIO
SEETHING	PRI AF	122.6	AG RADIO
TIBENHAM	CIV AF	129.97	AG RADIO
		130.1	GLIDERS
STANFORD	MIL STN	307.8	ARMY AG RADIO

AREA 8A

AIRFIELDS OF ANGLIA & COUNTIES N.E. OF LONDON

STATION	TYPE	FREQUENCY	SERVICE / REMARKS / CALL
HETHERSET	PRI AF	129.82	AG RADIO
MILDENHALL	MIL AF	122.55	TWR
		142.07	LAKENHEATH DEPS
		258.82	TWR
		370.25	TWR
		278.15	GRND
		142.27	ATIS
		277.07	ATIS
		398.35	APP / GCA
		365.1	OPS / DISPATCHER
		312.45	COMMAND POST
		344.8	COMMAND POST
		257.75	METRO
		242.07	LAKENHEATH DEPS
LAKENHEATH	MIL AF	122.1	TWR
		128.9	APP / MATZ
		137.2	APP
		123.3	PAR RADAR / SRE
		358.67	TWR
		257.8	TWR
		397.97	GRND
		264.67	MATZ
		249.7	ATIS
		257.75	MILDENHALL METRO
		300.82	OPS / DISPATCHER
		269.07	COMMAND POST
		242.07	APP
		337.6	APP
		309.07	PAR RADAR
		290.82	PAR RADAR
		338.67	PAR RADAR
		264.1	PAR RADAR
		279.25	PAR RADAR
NEWMARKET	PRI AF	129.05	HONNINGTON APP
CROWFIELD	PRI AF	122.77	AG RADIO
WATTISHAM	MIL AF	122.1	TWR
		125.8	APP
		123.3	DIR / PAR RADAR
		358.6	TWR
		291.12	APP

AREA 8A

AIRFIELDS OF ANGLIA & COUNTIES N.E. OF LONDON

STATION	TYPE	FREQUENCY	SERVICE / REMARKS / CALL
WATTISHAM (continued)		283.57	DIR
		356.17	PAR RADAR
		359.82	PAR RADAR
IPSWICH	CIV AP	118.32	TWR / APP / RAD
NUTHAMPSTEAD	PRI AF	123.05	AG RADIO
AUDLEY END	PRI AF	122.35	AG RADIO
EARLS COLNE	PRI AF	122.42	AG RADIO
CLACTON	CIV AF	122.32	AG RADIO

AMENDMENTS

STATION	TYPE	FREQUENCY	SERVICE / REMARKS / CALL

AREAS 9 & 9A

ZONES & AIRWAYS OF LONDON & S. E. ENGLAND

FREQUENCY	CALL	SERVICE
124.75	LONDON INFORMATION	SOUTH WEST
124.6	LONDON INFORMATION	SOUTH EAST
135.57	VOLMET (LONDON MAIN)	WEATHER
118.82	LONDON CONTROL	AIRWAYS CONTROL — A1, A2, A20, A30, A34, A47, A56, B3, B4, B71, B317, B321, G1, G27, H51, H52, H53, R1, R8, R25, R41, R84, R123, R803, W70
119.77	LONDON CONTROL	AIRWAYS CONTROL — A1, A2, A20, A30, A34, A47, A56, B3, B4, B71, B317, B321, G1, G27, H51, H52, H53, R1, R8, R25, R41, R84, R123, R803, W70
128.42	LONDON CONTROL	AIRWAYS CONTROL — A1, A2, A20, A30, A34, A47, A56, B3, B4, B71, B317, B321, G1, G27, H51, H52, H53, R1, R8, R25, R41, R84, R123, R803, W70
129.42	LONDON CONTROL	AIRWAYS CONTROL — A1, A2, A20, A30, A34, A47, A56, B3, B4, B71, B317, B321, G1, G27, H51, H52, H53, R1, R8, R25, R41, R84, R123, R803, W70
130.92	LONDON CONTROL	AIRWAYS CONTROL — A1, A2, A20, A30, A34, A47, A56, B3, B4, B71, B317, B321, G1, G27, H51, H52, H53, R1, R8, R25, R41, R84, R123, R803, W70
132.45	LONDON CONTROL	AIRWAYS CONTROL — A1, A2, A20, A30, A34, A47, A56, B3, B4, B71, B317, B321, G1, G27, H51, H52, H53, R1, R8, R25, R41, R84, R123, R803, W70
132.6	LONDON CONTROL	AIRWAYS CONTROL — A1, A2, A20, A30, A34, A47, A56, B3, B4, B71, B317, B321, G1, G27, H51, H52, H53, R1, R8, R25, R41, R84, R123, R803, W70
133.45	LONDON CONTROL	AIRWAYS CONTROL — A1, A2, A20, A30, A34, A47, A56, B3, B4, B71, B317, B321, G1, G27, H51, H52, H53, R1, R8, R25, R41, R84, R123, R803, W70
134.9	LONDON CONTROL	AIRWAYS CONTROL — A1, A2, A20, A30, A34, A47, A56, B3, B4, B71, B317, B321, G1, G27, H51, H52, H53, R1, R8, R25, R41, R84, R123, R803, W70

AREAS 9 & 9A

ZONES & AIRWAYS OF LONDON & S. E. ENGLAND

FREQUENCY	CALL	SERVICE
135.05	LONDON CONTROL	AIRWAYS CONTROL — A1, A2, A20, A30, A34, A47, A56, B3, B4, B71, B317, B321, G1, G27, H51, H52, H53, R1, R8, R25, R41, R84, R123, R803, W70
135.32	LONDON CONTROL	AIRWAYS CONTROL — A1, A2, A20, A30, A34, A47, A56, B3, B4, B71, B317, B321, G1, G27, H51, H52, H53, R1, R8, R25, R41, R84, R123, R803, W70
135.45	LONDON CONTROL	AIRWAYS CONTROL — A1, A2, A20, A30, A34, A47, A56, B3, B4, B71, B317, B321, G1, G27, H51, H52, H53, R1, R8, R25, R41, R84, R123, R803, W70
136.6	LONDON CONTROL	AIRWAYS CONTROL — A1, A2, A20, A30, A34, A47, A56, B3, B4, B71, B317, B321, G1, G27, H51, H52, H53, R1, R8, R25, R41, R84, R123, R803, W70
118.82	LONDON CONTROL	UPPER AIR ROUTES — UA1, UA2, UA20, UA30, UA34, UA37, UA39, UA47, UA56, UB4, UB11, UB39, UG1, UG27, UG39, UG106, UL613, UR1, UR8, UR25, UR37, UR41, UR84, UR123, UW550
119.77	LONDON CONTROL	UPPER AIR ROUTES — UA1, UA2, UA20, UA30, UA34, UA37, UA39, UA47, UA56, UB4, UB11, UB39, UG1, UG27, UG39, UG106, UL613, UR1, UR8, UR25, UR37, UR41, UR84, UR123, UW550
128.42	LONDON CONTROL	UPPER AIR ROUTES — UA1, UA2, UA20, UA30, UA34, UA37, UA39, UA47, UA56, UB4, UB11, UB39, UG1, UG27, UG39, UG106, UL613, UR1, UR8, UR25, UR37, UR41, UR84, UR123, UW550
129.42	LONDON CONTROL	UPPER AIR ROUTES — UA1, UA2, UA20, UA30, UA34, UA37, UA39, UA47, UA56, UB4, UB11, UB39, UG1, UG27, UG39, UG106, UL613, UR1, UR8, UR25, UR37, UR41, UR84, UR123, UW550

AREAS 9 & 9A

ZONES & AIRWAYS OF LONDON & S. E. ENGLAND

FREQUENCY	CALL	SERVICE
130.92	LONDON CONTROL	UPPER AIR ROUTES — UA1, UA2, UA20, UA30, UA34, UA37, UA39, UA47, UA56, UB4, UB11, UB39, UG1, UG27, UG39, UG106, UL613, UR1, UR8, UR25, UR37, UR41, UR84, UR123, UW550
132.45	LONDON CONTROL	UPPER AIR ROUTES — UA1, UA2, UA20, UA30, UA34, UA37, UA39, UA47, UA56, UB4, UB11, UB39, UG1, UG27, UG39, UG106, UL613, UR1, UR8, UR25, UR37, UR41, UR84, UR123, UW550
132.6	LONDON CONTROL	UPPER AIR ROUTES — UA1, UA2, UA20, UA30, UA34, UA37, UA39, UA47, UA56, UB4, UB11, UB39, UG1, UG27, UG39, UG106, UL613, UR1, UR8, UR25, UR37, UR41, UR84, UR123, UW550
133.45	LONDON CONTROL	UPPER AIR ROUTES — UA1, UA2, UA20, UA30, UA34, UA37, UA39, UA47, UA56, UB4, UB11, UB39, UG1, UG27, UG39, UG106, UL613, UR1, UR8, UR25, UR37, UR41, UR84, UR123, UW550
134.9	LONDON CONTROL	UPPER AIR ROUTES — UA1, UA2, UA20, UA30, UA34, UA37, UA39, UA47, UA56, UB4, UB11, UB39, UG1, UG27, UG39, UG106, UL613, UR1, UR8, UR25, UR37, UR41, UR84, UR123, UW550
135.05	LONDON CONTROL	UPPER AIR ROUTES — UA1, UA2, UA20, UA30, UA34, UA37, UA39, UA47, UA56, UB4, UB11, UB39, UG1, UG27, UG39, UG106, UL613, UR1, UR8, UR25, UR37, UR41, UR84, UR123, UW550
135.32	LONDON CONTROL	UPPER AIR ROUTES — UA1, UA2, UA20, UA30, UA34, UA37, UA39, UA47, UA56, UB4, UB11, UB39, UG1, UG27, UG39, UG106, UL613, UR1, UR8, UR25, UR37, UR41, UR84, UR123, UW550

AREAS 9 & 9A

ZONES & AIRWAYS OF LONDON & S. E. ENGLAND

FREQUENCY	CALL	SERVICE
135.45	LONDON CONTROL	UPPER AIR ROUTES — UA1, UA2, UA20, UA30, UA34, UA37, UA39, UA47, UA56, UB4, UB11, UB39, UG1, UG27, UG39, UG106, UL613, UR1, UR8, UR25, UR37, UR41, UR84, UR123, UW550
136.6	LONDON CONTROL	UPPER AIR ROUTES — UA1, UA2, UA20, UA30, UA34, UA37, UA39, UA47, UA56, UB4, UB11, UB39, UG1, UG27, UG39, UG106, UL613, UR1, UR8, UR25, UR37, UR41, UR84, UR123, UW550
132.7	THAMES RADAR	LONDON (CITY) & BIGGIN HILL
135.15	LONDON MILITARY	UPPER, MIDDLE & LOWER AIRSPACE SERVICE
275.47	LONDON MILITARY	UPPER, MIDDLE & LOWER AIRSPACE SERVICE
	LONDON CONTROL	LONDON TERMINAL AREA — INBOUND
120.17	LONDON CONTROL	VIA LUMBA, TIMBA
121.22	LONDON CONTROL	VIA LAMBOURNE
121.27	LONDON CONTROL	VIA BOVINGDON
130.92	LONDON CONTROL	VIA LONDON CITY, BIGGIN HILL & SOUTHEND
133.17	LONDON CONTROL	VIA WILLO
134.12	LONDON CONTROL	VIA OCKHAM
	LONDON CONTROL	LONDON TERMINAL AREA — OUTBOUND
118.82	LONDON CONTROL	VIA BROOKMANS PARK
119.77	LONDON CONTROL	VIA BOVINGDON
120.52	LONDON CONTROL	VIA DETLING
133.17	LONDON CONTROL	VIA MIDHURST, WORTHING
134.12	LONDON CONTROL	VIA COMPTON, SOUTHAMPTON
135.42	LONDON CONTROL	UPPER LONDON (WEST) (HIGH LEVEL OVER-FLIGHTS)
134.45	LONDON CONTROL	UPPER LONDON (EAST) (HIGH LEVEL OVER-FLIGHTS)

AREA 9

AIRFIELDS OF HOME COUNTIES & GREATER LONDON

STATION	TYPE	FREQUENCY	SERVICE / REMARKS / CALL
ANDREWSFIELD	CIV AF	130.55	AG RADIO
		122.55	STANSTED APP
SOUTHEND	CIV AP	127.72	TWR
		125.05	RAD
		121.8	ATIS. DEPARTURES
		128.95	APP / RAD
NORTH WEALD	CIV AF	123.52	AG RADIO
		129.97	GLIDERS
		130.17	ACEAIR
RUSH GREEN (HITCHIN)	CIV AF	122.35	AG RADIO
PANSHANGER	CIV AF	120.25	AG RADIO
STAPLEFORD	CIV AF	122.6	AG RADIO
		122.05	AEROMEGA OPS
HALTON	MIL AF	130.42	AG RADIO (CLUB FREQ)
		356.27	AG RADIO
SHENDISH (FELDEN)	PRI HELIPAD	129.75	AIRTOUR RADIO
ELSTREE	CIV AF	122.4	AG RADIO
LONDON CITY	CIV AP	127.95	TWR
		118.07	TWR
		132.7	APP THAMES RADAR
		128.02	CITY RADAR
LONDON BATTERSEA	CIV HELIPAD	122.9	TWR
		119.9	APP
MET POLICE		130.47	AG RADIO
LONDON HAYES	PRI HELIPAD	123.65	AG RADIO
NORTHOLT	MIL AF	126.45	TWR / APP
		124.97	DIR / GRND
		120.32	DIR / SRE
		130.35	DIRECTOR / PAR RAD
		120.32	DIRECTOR / PAR RAD
		300.35	ATIS
		125.87	PAR

AREA 9

AIRFIELDS OF HOME COUNTIES & GREATER LONDON

STATION	TYPE	FREQUENCY	SERVICE / REMARKS / CALL
NORTHOLT (continued)		312.35	TWR
		257.8	TWR
		244.42	OPS
		344.97	APP
		362.3	APP
		379.42	DIR
		375.5	PAR RADAR
		385.4	PAR RADAR
LONDON HEATHROW	CIV AP	118.7	TWR
		118.5	TWR
		124.47	TWR (AS INSTRUCTED)
		121.9	GRND
		121.7	GRND
		121.97	GRND.DEP INITIAL CALL
		119.72	DIRECTOR / APP
		120.4	DIRECTOR
		127.52	DIRECTOR / APP
		134.97	DIRECTOR / APP /RAD
		125.62	RAD
		123.9	ATIS
		115.1	ATIS (BIGGIN VOR)
		113.75	ATIS (BOVINGDON VOR)
		119.9	RAD (SPEC VFR & HELIS)
THAME	PRI AF	124.6	LONDON INFORMATION
DENHAM	CIV AF	130.72	AG RADIO
WYCOMBE AIR PARK	CIV AF	126.55	AG RADIO
		121.77	GRND
WHITE WALTHAM	CIV AF	122.6	AG RADIO

AREA 9A

AIRFIELDS OF HOME COUNTIES SOUTH OF LONDON

STATION	TYPE	FREQUENCY	SERVICE / REMARKS / CALL
MANSTON	MIL AF	119.27	TWR
		122.1	TWR / APP
		126.35	APP / RAD / LARS
		123.3	PAR RADAR
		344.35	TWR
		257.8	TWR
		231.6	APP
		362.3	APP
		129.45	APP
		119.92	PAR
		338.62	DIR / RAD
		344.0	DIR /RAD
		312.32	PAR RADAR
		385.4	PAR RADAR
ROCHESTER	PRI AF	122.25	AFIS
WEST MALLING	CIV AF	130.87	AG RADIO
BIGGIN HILL	CIV AF	134.8	TWR
		121.87	ATIS
		129.4	APP
		132.7	THAMES RADAR
REDHILL	CIV AF	120.27	TWR / AFIS
FAIROAKS	CIV AF	123.42	AG RADIO / AFIS
BLACKBUSHE	CIV AF	122.3	AFIS
FARNBOROUGH	MOD AF	122.5	TWR
		129.97	AG RADIO (GLIDERS)
		134.35	APP / PAR RADAR
		125.25	ATC / RAD / LARS
		130.37	FARNBO' EXECUTIVE
		130.05	APP / PAR RADAR
		357.4	TWR
		376.9	APP / LARS
		386.77	APP / ODIHAM RAD
		315.52	APP / RAD
		259.0	PAR RADAR
ODIHAM	MIL AF	122.1	TWR / APP
		125.25	FARNBO APP / MATZ
		309.62	TWR

AREA 9A

AIRFIELDS OF HOME COUNTIES SOUTH OF LONDON

STATION	TYPE	FREQUENCY	SERVICE / REMARKS / CALL
ODIHAM (continued)		257.8	TWR
		276.17	ATIS
		315.97	APP
		123.3	TALKDOWN
		386.77	RAD / SRE
		300.45	PAR RADAR
		385.4	PAR RADAR
POPHAM	CIV AF	129.8	AG RADIO

AREA 9A

AIRFIELDS OF SOUTH EAST & CENTRAL S. COAST

STATION	TYPE	FREQUENCY	SERVICE / REMARKS / CALL
CANTERBURY	PRI AF	126.3	MANSTON APP
LYDD	CIV AF	120.7	TWR / APP / AG RADIO
		131.3	TWR
DEANLAND	PRI AF	129.72	AG RADIO
LASHENDEN (HEADCORN)	CIV AF	122.0	AG RADIO
DUNSFOLD	PRI AF	124.32	TWR
		135.17	APP / RAD / LARS
		375.4	TWR
		367.37	APP / LARS
		312.62	APP / RAD
LONDON GATWICK	CIV AP	124.22	TWR
		134.22	TWR
		121.8	GRND
		121.95	DELIVERY
		136.52	ATIS
		126.82	DIRECTOR / APP
		129.02	DIRECTOR / APP
		135.57	DIRECTOR / APP
		118.95	DIRECTOR / APP

AREA 9A

AIRFIELDS OF SOUTH EAST & CENTRAL S. COAST

STATION	TYPE	FREQUENCY	SERVICE / REMARKS / CALL
LASHAM	PRI AF	122.87	AG RADIO
		129.90	AG (GLIDER OPS)
		125.25	FARNBOROUGH APP
SHOREHAM	CIV AF	123.15	TWR / APP / AG RADIO
		125.4	TWR (AS DIRECTED)
		132.4	ATIS
CHICHESTER	CIV AF	120.65	TWR
(GOODWOOD)		122.45	TWR / APP / AG RADIO
		125.87	DUNSFOLD APP / LARS
GOODWOOD RACECOURSE	PRI HELIPAD	130.5	AG RADIO
SOLENT AREA		120.22	SOLENT APPROACH
SOUTHAMPTON	CIV AP	118.2	TWR
		113.35	ATIS
			(SOUTHAMPTON VOR)
		131.0	APP
		128.85	APP / RAD
		120.22	SOLENT APP
		130.65	OPS
LEE ON SOLENT	MIL AF	135.7	TWR
		132.65	SAR
		3I5.65	TWR
FLEETLANDS	MIL HELIPAD	137.7	AG (LEE TWR)
		315.65	TWR AG (LEE TWR)
BEMBRIDGE (IOW)	PRI AF	123.25	AG RADIO
SANDOWN (IOW)	CIV AF	123.5	AG RADIO

AREAS 10 & 10A

ZONES & AIRWAYS OF S. W. ENGLAND & CHANNEL ISLANDS

FREQUENCY	CALL	SERVICE
124.75	LONDON INFORMATION	SOUTH WEST
135.37	VOLMET (LONDON MAIN)	WEATHER
128.6	VOLMET (LONDON SOUTH)	WEATHER
126.07	LONDON CONTROL	AIRWAYS CONTROL — A25, A34, B10, B11, B39, B321, G1, H51, R1, R8, R14, R25, R37, R41, R84, Y3
132.95	LONDON CONTROL	AIRWAYS CONTROL — A25, A34, B10, B11, B39, B321, G1, H51, R1, R8, R14, R25, R37, R41, R84, Y3
135.05	LONDON CONTROL	AIRWAYS CONTROL — A25, A34, B10, B11, B39, B321, G1, H51, R1, R8, R14, R25, R37, R41, R84, Y3
134.75	LONDON CONTROL	AIRWAYS CONTROL — A25, A34, B10, B11, B39, B321, G1, H51, R1, R8, R14, R25, R37, R41, R84, Y3
126.07	LONDON CONTROL	UPPER AIR ROUTES — UA25, UA29, UA34,UB10, UB11, UB39, UB40, UB321, UG1, UG4, UG45, UL3, UL607, UL722, UP2, UP4, UN502, UN512, UN862, UN863, UN865, UR1, UR8, UR14, UR25, UR37, UR40, UR41, UR72, UR84, UR107, UR116, UR168, UW501, UW502
132.95	LONDON CONTROL	UPPER AIR ROUTES — UA25, UA29, UA34,UB10, UB11, UB39, UB40, UB321, UG1, UG4, UG45, UL3, UL607, UL722, UP2, UP4, UN502, UN512, UN862, UN863, UN865, UR1, UR8, UR14, UR25, UR37, UR40, UR41, UR72, UR84, UR107, UR116, UR168, UW501, UW502
135.05	LONDON CONTROL	UPPER AIR ROUTES — UA25, UA29, UA34,UB10, UB11, UB39, UB40, UB321, UG1, UG4, UG45, UL3, UL607, UL722, UP2, UP4, UN502, UN512, UN862, UN863, UN865, UR1, UR8, UR14, UR25, UR37, UR40, UR41, UR72, UR84, UR107, UR116, UR168, UW501, UW502

ZONES & AIRWAYS OF S.W. ENGLAND & CHANNEL ISLANDS

FREQUENCY	CALL	SERVICE
134.75	LONDON CONTROL	UPPER AIR ROUTES — UA25, UA29, UA34,UB10, UB11, UB39, UB40, UB321, UG1, UG4, UG45, UL3, UL607, UL722, UP2, UP4, UN502, UN512, UN862, UN863, UN865, UR1, UR8, UR14, UR25, UR37, UR40, UR41, UR72, UR84, UR107, UR116, UR168, UW501, UW502
126.07	LONDON CONTROL	SUPERSONIC ROUTES — SL2, SL3, SL5
132.95	LONDON CONTROL	SUPERSONIC ROUTES — SL2, SL3, SL5
134.75	LONDON CONTROL	SUPERSONIC ROUTES — SL2, SL3, SL5
135.6	SHANNON CONTROL	SUPERSONIC ROUTES — SL2, SL3, SL5
125.2	JERSEY RADAR	JERSEY CTA
120.45	JERSEY RADAR	JERSEY CTA
124.7	SHANNON CONTROL	SHANNON OCEANIC TRANSITION AREA
131.15	SHANNON CONTROL	SHANNON OCEANIC TRANSITION AREA
134.27	SHANNON CONTROL	SHANNON OCEANIC TRANSITION AREA
135.6	SHANNON CONTROL	SHANNON OCEANIC TRANSITION AREA
135.15	LONDON MILITARY	UPPER, MIDDLE, & LOWER AIRSPACE SERVICE
275.47	LONDON MILITARY	UPPER, MIDDLE, & LOWER AIRSPACE SERVICE

AREA 10

AIRFIELDS OF SOUTH WESTERN COUNTIES

STATION	TYPE	FREQUENCY	SERVICE / REMARKS / CALL
NETHERAVON	MIL AF	128.3	TWR
		290.95	TWR
		282.25	SALISBURY PLAIN
SALISBURY PLAIN	MIL NO FIELD	122.75	AG RADIO
		282.25	AG RADIO
BOSCOMBE DOWN	MOD AF	130.75	TWR
		130.75	GRND
		126.7	APP / MATZ / LARS
		130.0	PAR RADAR
		386.7	TWR
		299.4	GRND
		263.5	ATIS
		359.77	APP / MATZ
		362.65	APP / ZONE / LARS
		276.85	PAR RADAR
		336.15	PAR RADAR
MIDDLE WALLOP	MIL AF	122.1	TWR / APP
		126.7	APP / BOSCOMBE ZONE
		372.62	TWR
		312.0	APP
		312.67	DIR / APP
		364.82	PAR RADAR
OLD SARUM	CIV AF	123.57	AG RADIO
		123.2	AG RADIO
		126.7	BOSCOMBE ZONE
BOURNEMOUTH	CIV AP	125.6	TWR
		121.7	GRND
		121.95	ATIS DEPARTURES
		119.62	APP / RAD
		118.65	RAD
COMPTON ABBAS	CIV AF	122.7	AG RADIO / AFIS
YEOVIL (JUDWIN) (WESTLAND)	CIV AF	125.4	TWR / AG RADIO
		130.8	APP / RAD
		127.35	YEOVILTON RAD / MATZ
		372.42	TWR
		369.97	APP / RAD
		300.67	RAD

AREA 10A

AIRFIELDS OF SOUTH WESTERN COUNTIES

STATION	TYPE	FREQUENCY	SERVICE / REMARKS / CALL
YEOVILTON	MIL AF	122.1	TWR
		127.35	APP / RAD / MATZ / LARS
		123.3	PAR RADAR
		372.65	TWR
		311.32	GRND
		379.75	ATIS
		369.87	APP / MATZ / LARS
		338.87	DIR
		362.3	DIR
		339.97	PAR RADAR
		344.35	PAR ARDAR
		8.977 KHz	AG RADIO / HF (SSB)
MERRYFIELD	MIL AF	122.1	TWR
		312.7	TWR
PORTLAND	MIL AF	122.1	TWR / APP / SRE
		123.3	TWR / APP
		124.15	TWR / APP / MATZ / SRE
		337.75	TWR
		362.3	APP / PAR RADAR
		300.17	APP / RAD / LARS
		312.4	PAR RADAR
		343.47	atis
		282.8	SAR AG RADIO
	HF STN	6688 KHz	AG RADIO (SSB)
	HF STN	6689.5 KHz	AG RADIO (SSB)
WESTON ZOYLAND		PRI AF	

AREA 10A

AIRFIELDS OF DEVON, CORNWALL & CHANNEL ISLANDS

STATION	TYPE	FREQUENCY	SERVICE / REMARKS / CALL
DUNKESWELL	CIV AF	123.47	AG RADIO
EXETER	CIV AP	119.8	TWR
		128.15	APP / RAD
		119.05	RAD
EAGLESCOTT	CIV AF	123.0	AG RADIO
DARTMOUTH	MIL HELIPAD	386.72	RN COLLEGE
CHIVENOR	MIL AF	130.2	CHIVENOR RESCUE
		252.8	CHIVENOR RESCUE
PLYMOUTH CITY	CIV AP	122.6	TWR
		133.55	APP
LISKEARD HELIPORT	CIV HELIPAD	129.9	AG RADIO
BODMIN	CIV AF	122.7	AG RADIO
ST. MAWGAN	MIL AF	123.4	TWR
		122.1	TWR / APP
		125.55	APP / RAD
		126.5	APP / MATZ / LARS
		252.52	ATIS
		123.3	DIRECTOR / PAR RADAR
		241.82	TWR
		376.62	GRND
		260.0	OPS
		357.2	APP / LARS
		360.55	DIR
		344.0	DIR
		387.45	PAR RADAR
		385.4	PAR RADAR
PERRANPORTH	PRI AF	119.75	AG RADIO
		130.1	GLIDER OPS
TRURO	PRI AF	129.8	AG RADIO
		134.05	CULDROSE APP
		126.5	ST MAWGAN APP
PREDANNICK	MIL AF	134.05	CULDROSE APP
		338.97	TWR
		370.0	TWR
		241.95	CULDROSE APP

AIRFIELDS OF DEVON, CORNWALL & CHANNEL ISLANDS

STATION	TYPE	FREQUENCY	SERVICE / REMARKS / CALL
CULDROSE	MIL AF	122.1	TWR / RAD
		123.3	TWR
		134.05	APP / RAD / LARS
		386.52	TWR
		299.4	GRND
		282.1	ATIS
		241.95	APP / LARS
		339.95	RAD
		388.0	PAR RADAR
		259.75	PAR RADAR
	HF STN	5696 KHz	AG RADIO (SSB)
LANDS END (ST JUST)	CIV AF	130.7	TWR / APP
PENZANCE (HELIPORT)	CIV HELIPORT	118.1	TWR
SCILLY ISLES (ST MARY'S)	CIV AP	123.15	TWR / APP
TRESCO	CIV HELIPAD	130.25	AG RADIO

AREA 10A

AIRFIELDS OF THE CHANNEL ISLANDS

STATION	TYPE	FREQUENCY	SERVICE / REMARKS / CALL
ALDERNEY	CIV AP	125.35	TWR
		128.65	GUERNSEY APP
GUERNSEY	CIV AP	119.95	TWR
		121.8	GRND
		109.4	ATIS
		128.65	APP
		124.5	APP / RAD / SRE
		118.9	RAD / SRE
JERSEY	CIV AP	119.45	TWR
		121.9	GRND
		112.2	ATIS JERSEY VOR
		120.3	APP / RAD
		118.55	ZONE
		120.45	ZONE
		125.2	APP

AREA 11

AIRFIELDS OF NORTHERN IRELAND

STATION	TYPE	FREQUENCY	SERVICE / REMARKS / CALL
BELFAST (CITY)	CIV AP	130.75	TWR
		130.85	APP
		134,8	RAD / SRE
BELFAST (ALDERGROVE)	CIV AP	118.3	TWR
		121.75	GRND
		128.2	ATIS
		120.0	APP
		120.9	RAD
		310.0	TWR / APP / RAD
		241.82	RAF OPS
NEWTONARDS	CIV AF	123.5	G RADIO
DUNDALK	CIV AF	122.9	AG RADIO
LONDONDERRY (EGLINGTON)	CIV AF	134.15	TWR
		123.62	APP
ENNISKILLEN (ST ANGELO)	CIV AF	123.2	AG RADIO

AREA 11

AIRFIELDS OF SOUTHERN IRELAND

STATION	TYPE	FREQUENCY	SERVICE / REMARKS / CALL
CARRICKFIN	PRI AF	129.8	AG RADIO
SLIGO	CIV AP	122.1	TWR
DONEGAL	CIV AF	129.8	TWR
BELMULLET	PRI AF	123.6	AG RADIO
CONNAUGHT (KNOCK)	CIV AP	130.7	TWR
		121.9	GRND
CASTLEBAR	CIV AF	122.6	AG RADIO
CONNEMARA	PRI AF	123.0	AG RADIO
GALWAY (CARNMORE)	CIV AP	122.5	AG RADIO / TWR

AREA 11

AIRFIELDS OF SOUTHERN IRELAND

STATION	TYPE	FREQUENCY	SERVICE / REMARKS / CALL
NISHMORE	PRI AF	123.0	AG RADIO
INISHIMAAN	PRI AF	123.0	AG RADIO
INISHEER	PRI AF	123.0	AG RADIO
ABBEYSHRULE	CIV AF	122.6	AG RADIO
CASTLEFORBES	PRI AF	130.5	AG RADIO
TRIM	PRI AF	123.3	AG RADIO
EDENDERRY	PRI AF	128.55	AG RADIO
HACKETSTOWN	PRI AF	128.8	DUBLIN CONTROL
		124.65	DUBLIN CONTROL
DUBLIN	CIV AP	118.6	TWR
		121.8	GRND
		124.52	ATIS
		121.1	APP
		119.55	RAD / DIRECTOR / SRE
		118.5	DIRECTOR / SRE
		124.65	DUBLIN CONTROL / ACC SOUTH
		129.17	DUBLIN CONTROL / ACC NORTH
		136.05	DUBLIN CONTROL (AS DIRECTED)
		136.15	DUBLIN CONTROL (AS DIRECTED)
DUBLIN (WESTON)	CIV AF	122.4	AG RADIO
		118.6	DUBLIN TWR
		128.0	DUBLIN CENTRE
		121.1	DUBLIN DIRECTOR
BALDONNEL / CASEMENT	MIL AF	123.5	TWR
		123.1	GRND
		122.0	APP
		122.8	RAD
		122.3	RAD (DUBLIN MILITARY)
		129.7	BALDONNEL TALKDOWN
POWERSCOURT	PRI AF	123.65	AG RADIO
SPANISH POINT	CIV AF	123.3	AG RADIO
		124.7	FIS. SHANNON CONTROL
RATHCOOLE	PRI AF	124.7	SHANNON CONTROL
SHANNON AREA CONTROL CENTRE		131.15	CORK SECTOR
		135.6	SOTA SECTOR
		134.27	SHANNON SECTOR

AREA 11

AIRFIELDS OF SOUTHERN IRELAND

STATION	TYPE	FREQUENCY	SERVICE / REMARKS / CALL
SHANNON AREA **CONTROL CENTRE** (continued)		124.7	SHANNON SECTOR
		132.15	BABAN/DEVOL SECTOR
		127.5	CORK SECTOR
		121.7	CENTRE OCEANIC DEL
		135.22	SOTA SECTOR
SHANNON	CIV AP	118.7	TWR
		121.8	GRND
		130.95	ATIS
		121.7	SHANNON CONTROL
		121.4	APP / RAD DIR
		120.2	APP
GOWRAN GRANGE	PRI AF	130.4	AG RADIO (GLIDERS)
BALLYFREE	PRI AF	122.9	AG RADIO
BIRR	CIV AF	122.95	AG RADIO
LIMERICK (COONAGH)	PRI AF	129.9	AG RADIO
		120.2	SHANNON APP
KILKENNY	CIV AF	122.9	AG RADIO
		130.4	GLIDERS
FETHARD	PRI AF	123.3	AG RADIO
CASTLEBRIDGE	PRI AF	123.0	AG RADIO
WATERFORD	CIV AP	129.85	TWR / AFIS
FARRANFORE	CIV AF	122.6	TWR
BANTRY	PRI AF	122.4	AG RADIO
KERRY	CIV AP	124.1	GRND
CORK	CIV AP	119.3	TWR
		121.7	TWR
		120.92	ATIS
		121.8	GRND
		119.9	APP
		118.8	RAD / SRE
KILBRITTAIN	PRI AF	122.9	AG RADIO

NORTH ATLANTIC REGION

HIGH FREQUENCY ALLOCATIONS AND OCEANIC CLEARANCE FREQUENCIES

FREQUENCY	CALL	SERVICE
123.95	SHANWICK	CLEARANCE DELIVERY (AMERICAN / CANADIAN AIRLINES)
127.65	SHANWICK	CLEARANCE DELIVERY (EUROPEAN AIRLINES)
135.52	SHANWICK	CLEARANCE DELIVERY (SELECTED AIRLINES ONLY)

NOTE: MESSAGES ON THESE FREQUENCIES MAY BE HEARD THROUGHOUT THE UK.

3016	SHANWICK	FAMILY A — SOUTHERN ROUTES
5598	SHANWICK	FAMILY A — SOUTHERN ROUTES
8906	SHANWICK	FAMILY A — SOUTHERN ROUTES
13306	SHANWICK	FAMILY A — SOUTHERN ROUTES
17946	SHANWICK	FAMILY A — SOUTHERN ROUTES
2899	SHANWICK	FAMILY B — CENTRAL & NORTHERN ROUTES
5616	SHANWICK	FAMILY B — CENTRAL & NORTHERN ROUTES
8864	SHANWICK	FAMILY B — CENTRAL & NORTHERN ROUTES
11279	SHANWICK	FAMILY B — CENTRAL & NORTHERN ROUTES
13291	SHANWICK	FAMILY B — CENTRAL & NORTHERN ROUTES
17946	SHANWICK	FAMILY B — CENTRAL & NORTHERN ROUTES
2872	SHANWICK	FAMILY C — CENTRAL & NORTHERN ROUTES
5649	SHANWICK	FAMILY C — CENTRAL & NORTHERN ROUTES
8879	SHANWICK	FAMILY C — CENTRAL & NORTHERN ROUTES
11336	SHANWICK	FAMILY C — CENTRAL & NORTHERN ROUTES
13306	SHANWICK	FAMILY C — CENTRAL & NORTHERN ROUTES
17946	SHANWICK	FAMILY C — CENTRAL & NORTHERN ROUTES
2971	SHANWICK	FAMILY D — CENTRAL & NORTHERN ROUTES

4675	SHANWICK	FAMILY D — CENTRAL & NORTHERN ROUTES
8891	SHANWICK	FAMILY D — CENTRAL & NORTHERN ROUTES
11279	SHANWICK	FAMILY D — CENTRAL & NORTHERN ROUTES
13291	SHANWICK	FAMILY D — CENTRAL & NORTHERN ROUTES
17946	SHANWICK	FAMILY D — CENTRAL & NORTHERN ROUTES
3476	SHANWICK	FAMILY F — CENTRAL & NORTHERN ROUTES
6622	SHANWICK	FAMILY F — CENTRAL & NORTHERN ROUTES
8831	SHANWICK	FAMILY F — CENTRAL & NORTHERN ROUTES
13291	SHANWICK	FAMILY F — CENTRAL & NORTHERN ROUTES
17946	SHANWICK	FAMILY F — CENTRAL & NORTHERN ROUTES
127.9	SHANWICK	VHF FREQUENCY (WHEN IN RANGE)

AMENDMENTS

STATION	TYPE	FREQUENCY	SERVICE / REMARKS / CALL

COMMUNICATION COMMON FREQUENCIES

FREQUENCY   USAGE

FREQUENCY	USAGE
118.0	AIR TO AIR
122.1	RAF TOWERS & APPROACH (STANDBY)
121.5	INTERNATIONAL EMERGENCY
121.6	FIRE & RESCUE
123.1	INTERNATIONAL SAR
123.3	RAF RADARS (STANDBY)
125.05	SOUTHEND AIR PAGEANTS
129.7	TRINITY HOUSE HELICOPTERS
129.9	UK BALLOONS (COMMON FREQUENCY)
130.1	UK GLIDERS (COMMON FREQUENCY)
130.12	UK GLIDERS (COMMON FREQUENCY)
130.4	UK GLIDERS (COMMON FREQUENCY)
130.42	UNICOM (SCENE OF EMERGENCY)
131.8	AIR TO AIR (INTERNATIONAL COMMON FREQUENCY)
138.7	NATO SCENE OF SEARCH & RESCUE
240.4	AIR TO AIR REFUELLING
243.45	RED ARROWS DISPLAY TEAM
243.0	NATO INTERNATIONAL EMERGENCY
244.0	UK SAR
244.6	SCENE OF SEARCH & RESCUE
252.8	NATO SAR (TRAINING)
252.9	BRITISH ARMY
255.1	ARMY AIR
257.8	NATO TWRS (COMMON FREQUENCY STANDBY)
259.7	NASA (SPACE SHUTTLE)
282.8	NATO (SAR TRAINING)
285.85	BOULMER RESCUE (AG)
294.8	AIR TO AIR REFUELLING
296.8	SPACE SHUTTLE (VOICE)
297.8	RESCUE
303.0	AIR TO AIR REFUELLING
306.5	AIR TO AIR REFUELLING
316.35	AIR TO AIR REFUELLING (USAF)
317.2	AIR TO AIR REFUELLING (USAF)
326.9	AIR TO AIR REFUELLING
344.0	NATO RADARS (COMMON FREQUENCY STANDBY)
344.1	AIR TO AIR REFUELLING
362.3	NATO APPROACHES (COMMON FREQUENCY STANDBY)
380.8	AIR TO AIR REFUELLING
385.4	NATO PAR RADARS (COMMON FREQUENCY STANDBY)
394.8	AIR TO AIR REFUELLING

AIRCRAFT RECOGNITION SECTION

Aérospatiale/BAC Concorde

Four turbojet supersonic airliner
Basic data for Concorde 102
Powerplant: Four Rolls-Royce/SNECMA Olympus 593 Mk 602 (reheat) turbojets of 169.3kN (38,050lb st)
Span: 83ft 10in (25.56m)
Length: 203ft 9in (62.10m)
Max Cruise: 1,336mph (2,179km/h) (Mach 2.04)
Passengers: 100 (plus three crew)
First aircraft flown: 2 March 1969 (French 001); 9 April 1969 (British 102). Entered service with Air France and British Airways 21 January 1976
Production: Two prototypes, two pre-production and 14 production aircraft
Recent/current service with: Air France (six) and British Airways (seven)
Recognition: Underwing mounted engines in two double nacelles. Slender, low-set delta wing. Narrow fuselage with pointed nose that droops for landing. No tailplane, angular fin and rudder. Very tall stalky undercarriage
Variants: None

Airbus A340

Four turbofan very long-range airliner
Basic data for Airbus A340-300
Powerplant: Four CFMI CFM56-5C2 turbofans of 138.8kN (31,200lb st)
Span: 197ft 10in (60.30m)
Length: 208ft 11in (63.6m)
Max Cruise: 568mph (914km/h) (Mach 0.86)
Passengers: Up to 440 plus two crew
First aircraft flown: 1 April 1992 (A340-200); 25 October 1991 (A340-300)
Production: First airline delivery in January 1993 (A340-200) and February 1993 (A340-300). 178 ordered by 21 airlines, with 87 delivered by late-1996
Recent/current service with: Entered service in 1993 with Air France. Subsequent service with Air Lanka, Air Mauritius, Air Portugal, Brunei, Cathay Pacific, Gulf Air, Iberia, Kuwait Airways, Lufthansa, Singapore Airlines, THY and Virgin Atlantic
Recognition: Four underwing podded engines in nacelles protruding forward of the leading edge. Long circular narrow body fuselage tapering towards the tail. Low-set swept (30deg) wings of narrow chord with winglets at the tips and five trailing edge fairings. Tall, swept fin and rudder set forward of tail cone. Swept tailplane with dihedral. Similar to A330 but with four engines
Variants: A340-200 seating 250-300 passengers, has the longest range of any commercial airliner in service. A340-300 is 14ft (4.3m) longer, seating 300-350 passengers and carrying up to 15.5 tonnes of cargo over 7,000 nautical miles. A340 Combi is available with a maximum payload of 66 tonnes. Optional engines CFM56-5C3 or -5C4 turbofans. An A340-8000 ultra-long range aircraft is now on offer, launched in November 1995 and for delivery in 1997. Future plans include an A340-600 with a new wing and engines, with a stretched A300 airframe

An Aerospatiale/BAC Concorde with the new tail logo in British Airways service.
Peter R. March

Airbus A340 in clean configuration after take-off. *Peter R. March*

Antonov An-124 Ruslan

Four turbofan long-range heavy cargo transport
Basic data for Antonov An-124-100 Ruslan
Powerplant: Four ZMKB Progress D-18T turbofans of 229kN (51,590lb st)
Span: 240ft 5¾in (73.30m)
Length: 226ft 8½in (69.10m)
Max Cruise: 537mph (865km/h)
First aircraft flown: 26 December 1982
Production: Production by late 1996, 48 of the 50 ordered
Recent/current service with: In service with Aeroflot, VTA, Air Foyle, HeavyLift Airlines, Polet, Volga-DNEPR and Moscow AW.
Recognition: The world's largest production aircraft. The configuration is similar to the Lockheed C-5 Galaxy ie: high, swept wing with four large underslung podded engines. Swept fin and rudder. Low-mounted tailplane. Upward hinged nose loading door, with a rear fuselage ramp/door for simultaneous front and rear loading and unloading. Twenty-four wheels on main undercarriage
Variants: Discussions are continuing with a programme to re-engine with GE CF6-80C2 turbofans. A 'westernised' An-124, known as the An-130, will have a four-man flight deck crew, instead of the usual six, and feature modern avionics

Boeing 747-400

Four turbofan very long-range airliner
Basic data for Boeing 747-400
Powerplant: Four 254kN (56,750lb st) Pratt & Whitney PW4056, 251kN (57,900lb st) General Electric CF6-80C2B1F, 258 kN (58,000lb st) Rolls-Royce RB211-524G or 270kN (60,000lb st) RB211-524H turbofans
Span: 211ft 5in (64.44m)
Length: 231ft 10in (70.70m)
Max Cruise: 583mph (938km/h)
Passengers: 421 plus two flight crew
First aircraft flown: 29 April 1988
Production: The 747-400 is the only version marketed since May 1990. Over 365 delivered by late-1996 and over 160 on order
Recent/current service with: Includes Air Canada, Air China, Air France, Air New Zealand, All Nippon, British Airways, Cathay Pacific, China AL, El Al, Japan AL, KLM, Korean Air, Lufthansa, Malaysian AL, Northwest AL, QANTAS, Saudi, Singapore Int AL, South African AW, Thai Int, United and Virgin Atlantic
Recognition: Underwing mounted engines in four separate nacelles. Swept, low-set wing with winglets, canted 22° outward and swept 60°. Upper deck extended rearwards by 7.11m (23ft 4in) compared with other versions. Tall swept fin with a fuselage mounted tailplane below the rudder. The wing has a special aerofoil and 3.66m (12ft 0in) greater span than the 747-200
Variants: The 747-400F combines the short upper deck of the -200F with the stronger and larger wing of the -400. The 747-400 Combi is a passenger/freight version. Boeing is studying longer-range and stretched versions of the 747, known as the 747-500X and -600X respectively

The An-124 is the largest four-engined cargo aircraft in regular airline service.
Peter R. March

A Boeing 747-412 in Singapore Airways colours. *Peter R. March*

This BAe146-200 is in the colours of Jersey European. *Peter R. March*

British Aerospace 146

Four turbofan short-medium range airliner
Basic data for BAe 146-300
Powerplant: Four 31kN (6,970lb st) Textron Lycoming ALF 502R-5 turbofans
Span: 86ft 5in (26.34m)
Length: 101ft 8in (30.99m)
Max Cruise: 493mph (797km/h)
Passengers: 103 plus two crew (128 in high density version)
First aircraft flown: BAe 146-100 3 September 1981; 146-200 1 August 1982; 146-300 1 May 1987
Production: 221 were built and delivered. Production superseded by Avro International Aerospace's Avroliner range (Avro is a division of BAe Regional Aircraft)
Recent/current service with: 200 in service with 22 airlines worldwide
Recognition: Underwing mounted engines in four nacelles. Slightly swept wings mounted on top of the fuselage, drooping towards the wing tips. Distinctive trailing edge wing fillets. The fuselage is circular in section with bulges on the lower side to accommodate the undercarriage. The rectangular fin and rudder is slightly swept with a T-tailplane mounted on top of the fin. Sideways-opening airbrakes below the rudder
Variants: Series 100, designed to operate from short or semi-prepared airstrips with minimal ground facilities — seating 82/94; **Series 200**, fuselage lengthened by 2.39m (7ft 10in) and seating 82/112; **Series 300**, development of Series 100 with increased length and seating 103/128. **Statesman**, executive version of all series. **146-QT Quiet Trader**, freighter version of all series; **146/QC Convertible**, convertible passenger/freight version of Series 200-QT and 300-QT. Early BAe 146s are being upgraded by British Aerospace Asset Management Jets particularly a cockpit upgrade with satellite-based navigation systems

The 'military' glazed lower nose on this Aeroflot Il-76MA indicates dual military and airline use. *Peter R. March*

Ilyushin Il-76
Four turbofan long-range transport
Basic data for Ilyushin Il-76T
Powerplant: Four Aviadvigatel D-30KP1 of 26,455lb st (118kN) turbofans
Span: 165ft 8in (50.50m)
Length: 152ft 10.5in (46.60m)
Max Cruise: 497mph (800km/h)
Payload: 88,185lb or 90 passengers and five crew
First aircraft flown: 25 March 1971
Production: Over 500 Il-76s built for civil airline use and at least 350 military Il-76-M variants. 350 in airline service mid-1996.
Recent/current service with: 19 airlines worldwide
Recognition: Underwing mounted engines in four nacelles. Slightly swept wings mounted on top of the fuselage, drooping towards the wing tips. Circular fuselage with large bulges on either side and below the lower fuselage section for the undercarriage. Rectangular swept fin and rudder on the raised rear fuselage, with the swept T-tailplane mounted on top of the fin. A bullet fairing projects forward from the junction of the fin and tailplane. The nose has distinctive windows in the lower half with a bulge behind
Variants: The Il-76TD has internal cabin improvements and marginally better performance. The Il-76MD is a military version that appears in Aeroflot colours. Ilyushin has plans to re-engine the Il-76 with CFMI CFM 56 turbofans and is actively replacing the DK-30s in 20 of the Russian airline's fleet with Perm PS-90A turbofans. The stretched (6.6m/21ft 8in) Il-76MF first flew in August 1995 and can seat up to 140 passengers. Powered by 156.9kN (35,232lb st) Aviadvigatel PS-90AN or 138.8kN (30,988lb st) CFM International CFM56 turbofans

McDonnell Douglas MD-11

Three turbofan long-range airliner
Basic data for MD-11
Powerplant: Three General Electric CF6-80C2D1F of 61,500lb st (274kN) or Pratt & Whitney PW4460 turbofans of 60,000lb st (267kN)
Span: 169ft 10in (51.70m)
Length: 200ft 11in (61.24m)
Max Cruise: 578mph (930km/h)
Passengers: 250 to 405 maximum plus two crew
First aircraft flown: 10 January 1990
Production: 157 delivered by late-1996, with orders for 17 outstanding
Recent/current service with: 24 airlines worldwide
Recognition: Two engines in underwing nacelles close to fuselage, one engine mounted on the fin above the fuselage with a straight-through exhaust pipe to the rear. A circular, wide-body fuselage with low-set, swept wings. Tailplane mid-set on the rear fuselage below the fin. Winglets are fitted
Variants: The basic MD-11 has a DC-10 Srs 30 fuselage lengthened by 18ft 9in (5.71m). Combi and freighter variants are also in production. A series of longer range MD-11ERs, including a stretched version, was available from early 1996. MDC has unveiled plans for an MD-11LRR — a longer-range and stretched version of the MD-11. This variant will have more powerful engines. A twin-engined short-fuselage variant has been announced. The MD-12 development is a high density version with modified wings and four engines

Tupolev Tu-154

Three turbofan medium-range airliner
Basic data for Tupolev Tu-154M
Powerplant: Three Aviadvigatel D-30KU-154-II turbofans of 23,380lb st (104kN)
Span: 123ft 1.75in (37.55m)
Length: 157ft (47.90m)
Max Cruise: 590mph (950km/h)
Passengers: 168-180 plus three crew
First aircraft flown: 4 October 1968; 1983 (Tu-154M)
Production: Over 1,000 Tu-154s (A, B and M) built of which nearly 400 are Tu-154Ms, which variant remains in production. It is due to be replaced by the Tu-204.
Recent/current service with: Over 750 in service with Aeroflot Russian Int'l and its many successor airlines; also operated by Air Ukraine, Armenian AL, Balkan Bulgarian, China NW, China SW, China United, CSA, Cubana, Far East Avia, Iran Air, Iran Air Tours, Kazakhstan AL, Krasnoyarsk AL, LOT, Malev and Syrianair, Tarom and Uzbekistan AW
Recognition: Two engines mounted either side of the rear fuselage with the third engine on top of the rear fuselage forward of the fin, exhausting through tail cone. Very swept wings set below the circular, narrow body fuselage. Fairings for the undercarriage extend to the rear of the wings. A swept T-tailplane mounted on top of the fin and rudder with a bullet fairing projecting forward of the tailplane/fin intersection. The wings appear to droop towards the tips
Variants: The three original versions operated in the West, the Tu-154, Tu-154A and Tu-154B, have no significant external differences, the main changes being in powerplant and internal improvements. The Tu-154M has a modified tailplane and spoilers. A cargo conversion, the Tu-154S, has a large port-side forward freight door

A MD-11 of Malaysia at Hong Kong. *Peter R. March*

The tail-mounted engines and a highly swept tailplane are evident on this Czech
Tu-154. *Daniel J. March*

Airbus A320

Twin turbofan medium-range airliner
Basic data for Airbus A320-200
Powerplant: Two CFMI CFM56-5B4 27,400lb st (122kN) turbofans or IAE V2500-A1, IAE V2527-A5 or CFM International CFM56-5B4 alternatives
Span: 111ft 10in (34.10m)
Length: 123ft 3in (37.57m)
Max Cruise: 561mph (903km/h)
Passengers: 180 maximum plus two crew
First aircraft flown: 22 February 1987
Production: By mid-1996 a total of 550 A320 had been delivered with 135 on order.
Recent/current service: With 67 airlines including Adria, Aero Lloyd, Air 2000, Air Canada, Air France, Air Inter, Air Malta, Airtours, Airworld, Alitalia, All Leisure, All Nippon AW, America West, Ansett AL, Balkan Bulgarian AL, British Airways, Caledonian AW, Canada 3000, Canadian Int'l AL, Cyprus AW, Dragonair, Egypt Air, Eurocypria, Gulf Air, Iberia, Indian Airlines, Kuwait AW, Lufthansa, Mexicana, Monarch, Northwest AL, Premiair, Royal Jordanian, South African AW, Swiss Air, TAP Air Portugal, Transasia, Tunis Air, United AL and Vietnam AL.
Recognition: Underwing mounted engines in nacelles protruding forward of the wings. Circular narrow body fuselage tapering upwards towards the tail. Low-set, swept wings of narrow chord with three trailing edge fairings and winglets. Tall, swept fin and rudder set forward of tail cone. Swept tailplane with dihedral
Variants: The A320-100 is the 130/140-seat version, only 21 of which were built

Boeing 737-300/400/500

Twin turbofan medium-range airliner
Basic data for Boeing 737-300
Powerplant: Two CFM56-3C-1 turbofans of 22,000lb st (98kN)
Span: 94ft 9in (28.88m)
Length: 109ft 7in (33.40m)
Max Cruise: 564mph (908km/h)
Passengers: Up to 149 plus two crew
First aircraft flown: 24 February 1984 (-300), 19 February 1988 (-400), 20 June 1989 (-500)
Production: Nearly 1681 delivered by mid-1996 with further orders at over 241
Recent/current service with: More than 120 airlines worldwide
Recognition: Large engines, with oval nacelles, noticeably flat at bottom to increase ground clearance, mounted under and forward of the swept wings. Circular fuselage with wings set in the lower section. Tall, angular, slightly swept fin and rudder with a pronounced dorsal fin. Swept tailplane set on the rear fuselage at base of rudder
Variants: 737-400 series is 10ft (3m) longer than the -300 accommodating 168 passengers in its 119ft 7in (36.4m) fuselage, and powered by two CFM56-3C turbofans of 23,500lb st (104.5kN). The -500 series has the short fuselage of the 200, with two CFM56-3-B1 turbofans of 20,000lb st (89kN). It carries up to 132 passengers in the all-economy version, or 108 in mixed-class configuration. First delivery was February 1990 to South West Airlines

An Airbus A320-211 in the colours of Iberia. *Peter R. March*

The shorter fuselage of the latest production Boeing 737 identifies it as a series 500.
Peter R. March

Boeing 767

Twin turbofan medium/long-range airliner

Basic data for Boeing 767-300ER

Powerplant: Two General Electric CF6-80C2B6F turbofans rated at 56,362lb st (251kN) or two 60,179lb st (268kN) Pratt & Whitney PW4060 turbofans

Span: 156ft 1in (47.57m)

Length: 180ft 3in (54.94m)

Max Cruise: 565mph (910km/h)

Passengers: Max of 328 plus two crew

First aircraft flown: 26 September 1981 (767-200); 30 January 1986 (767-300)

Production: 724 ordered of which 630 had been delivered by late-1996

Recent/current service with: Over 70 airlines including Aeroflot Russian Int'l, Air Algerie, Air Canada, Air China, Air Europa, Air Europe Italy, Air France, Air New Zealand, Airtours Intl, Alitalia, American Airlines, Ansett Worldwide, Asiana, All Nippon, Balkan Bulgarian AL, British Airways, Britannia, Canadian AL Intl, Condor Flug, Delta, Egyptair, El Al, Ethiopian, Gulf Air, Japan AL, KLM, Kuwait Airways, Lauda Air, Leisure Intl, LTU-Sud, LOT, Malev, Martinair, Qantas, Royal Brunei, SAS, Spanair, TransBrasil, TWA, United Airlines, USAir and VARIG

Recognition: Turbofans mounted under the swept wings. Circular fuselage (bulkier than the 757) with the wings set in the lower section, mid-way between the nose and tail. Very tall swept fin with the tailplane set on the rear fuselage at base of rudder

Variants: The original 767-200 200/210 seat version had a length of 48.51m (159ft 2in). British Airways was the launch customer (11) for a Rolls-Royce RB-211-535 engined version of the 767-300ER (extended range). The 767-300F freighter entered service with launch customer UPS in October 1995. It has a large forward port side freight door but no cabin windows. Boeing is projecting the 767-400X development (the second stretch) with a larger, re-designed wing including winglets, more powerful engines and other refinements to fly faster over a greater range (9,600km) and with a higher payload (25% more cargo or 10% lower seat kilometre costs)

A Boeing 767-336ER (extended range) of British Airways. *Peter R March*

The triple bogie wheels are evident on this Cathay Pacific Boeing 777. *Peter R. March*

Boeing 777
Twin turbofan long-range high-capacity airliner
Basic data for Boeing 777-200
Powerplant: Two 84,655lb st (377kN) GE Aircraft Engines GE90-85B or 76,796lb st (342kN) Pratt & Whitney PW4077 turbofans. Other powerplants possible
Span: 199ft 11in (61.00m)
Length: 209ft 1in (63.73m)
Max Cruise: 572mph (923km/h)
Passengers: 440 plus two crew
First aircraft flown: 12 June 1994
Production: 40 delivered by mid-1996 with over 281 on order
Recent/current service with: Entered service with United Airlines in June 1995 and British Airways in November 1995. Also in service, All Nippon AL, Cathay Pacific, China Southern AL, Emirates, Japan Air Lines and Thai Int
Recognition: The world's largest twin jet. Six mainwheels on each bogie. New wing of 31.6° sweepback. Cylindrical fuselage wider than 767. Outer wings fold to vertical to reduce gate width requirement at airports. Very tall swept fin with the tailplane set on the rear fuselage at the base of the rudder
Variants: The 200 IGW (increased gross-weight version) with longer range entered service with BA in September 1996. The 300 series, announced at the 1995 Paris air show, is capable of seating 420 passengers in a three-class layout, and is 3m longer than the 747. Engines to include 400kN Rolls-Royce Trent 890 turbofans as an option

Fokker 70/100

Twin turbofan short/medium-range airliner
Basic data for Fokker 70 (standard)
Powerplant: Two 61.6kN (13,850lb st) Rolls-Royce Tay 620 turbofans
Span: 92ft 11.5in (28.08m)
Length: 101ft 5in (30.91m)
Max Cruise: 531mph (854km/h)
Passengers: 80 plus two crew
First aircraft flown: 2 April 1993
Production: By late 1996 - 362 had been ordered with 297 delivered
Recent/current service: Air Inter, Air Littoral, Air UK, American AL, Austrian AL, British Midland, China Eastern, Corse, Deutsche BA, Iran Air, KLM CityHopper, Korean Air, Malev, Merpati Nusantara, Mexicana, Pelita AS, Portugalia, Sempati Air, Swissair, TAT European AL, Transwede, Tyrolean AW, US Air
Recognition: Engines mounted on the sides of the rear fuselage aft of the wing. Swept tailplane set at top of the fin which has a rounded top and dorsal fillet. Longer fuselage than the F28, circular in section, low-set swept wings
Variants: The Fokker 100 is 15ft 3in (4.62m) longer and seats 107 passengers. It first flew on 30 November 1986. This superseded the F28-4000, from which it was derived. The Fokker 70ER is the Extended Range version. Fokker Executive Jet 70/Jet 100 are the corporate shuttle, business and VIP versions. Fokker 130 is a proposed stretched derivative of the Fokker 100. This major Dutch manufacturer is in administrative receivership but the line should remain open until April 1997. A possible take over by Samsung of South Korea was blocked by the Government in January 1997

SATIC A300-600ST *Beluga*

Twin-turbofan very large transport aircraft
Basic data for SATIC A-300-600ST
Powerplant: Two 57,484lb st (256kN) GE Aircraft Engines CF6-80C2A8 turbofans
Span: 147ft 2in (44.84m)
Length: 184ft 3in (56.15m)
Max Cruise: 484.15mph (778.8km/h) (0.7M)
Payload: 47,098kg (47t/103,616lb)
First aircraft flown: 13 September 1994
Production: Production of the Special Aircraft Transport International Company A300-600 Super Transport *Beluga* — undertaken by the Aérospatiale/Daimler-Benz Aerospace 50:50 consortium, SATIC. Two examples built and delivered by mid-1996, with the third due April 1997 and fourth due June 1998, of the four ordered
Recent/current service with: The first four to be operated by Airbus Industrie to carry large aircraft — sub assemblies. SATIC is marketing the aircraft commercially
Recognition: Based on new-build A300-600R airframes with an upward-opening nose-section, 7.4m diameter fuselage, and a lowered flightdeck based on that of the A320. An enlarged fin and horizontal-tail end-plates to improve directional stability. Has 400cu metres greater volume than that of the Super Guppy and 22.5t greater payload capacity
Variants: None

A Fokker 100 flown by Air UK on its european services. *Daniel J. March*

The massive fuselage is well illustrated in this view of the SATIC Beluga. *Peter R. March*

De Havilland Canada Dash 7

Four turboprop STOL short-range airliner
Basic data for DHC Dash 7-100
Powerplant: Four 857kW (1,150shp) Pratt & Whitney PT6A-50 turboprops
Span: 93ft 0in (28.35m)
Length: 80ft 8in (24.59m)
Max Cruise: 265mph (426km/h)
Passengers: 50 plus two crew
First aircraft flown: 27 March 1975
Production: 111 built for 35 customers in 22 countries. Production ceased in 1988
Recent/current service: 76 in current service with Adria Airways, Air Niugini, Atlantic Southeast, British Airways/Brymon, Greenlandair, Grönlandsfly, Paradise Island AW, Piedmont AL, Pelita AS, Tyrolean AW, Wideroe and others
Recognition: Four turboprops, each with four-blade propellers, mounted below the straight wing, which has distinctive trailing flaps. The circular fuselage is set below the wing, tapering upwards towards the tail. Very large swept fin and rudder with a dorsal extension; a straight tailplane is mounted on top of the fin
Variants: Initial production aircraft were either Series 100 passenger or Series 101 cargo variants. These were superseded by the Series 150 and 151, which offered higher operating weights and fuel capacity

Avions de Transport Regional ATR 42

Twin turboprop regional airliner
Basic data for ATR 42-300
Powerplant: Two Pratt & Whitney Canada PW120-2 turboprops of 1,491kW (2,000shp)
Span: 80ft 7in (24.57m)
Length: 74ft 4½in (22.67m)
Max Cruise: 307mph (495km/h) at 20,000ft
Passengers: Maximum seating for 50 plus two crew
First aircraft flown: 16 August 1984; July 1995 (ATR42-400)
Production: 275 produced for 61 airlines by mid-1996 with a further 27 on order
Recent/current service with: Aeromar, Air Caledonie, Air Littoral, Air Tahiti, American Eagle, ATI, Aviana, British Airways/Cityflyer Express, Brittany Air Intl, Canadian Regional AL, Cimber Air, Continental Express, Croatia, CSA, Eurowings, Flagship AL, Gill Airways, Inter-Canadian, Lufthansa Cityline, Olympic Aviation, RFG, Titan, Trans World Express and other commuter airlines
Recognition: High set straight wing with slim engines projecting forward and below the wing close inboard. Circular section fuselage with large undercarriage fairings under the centre section. Distinctive, large, slightly swept fin and rudder with two angle changes on the forward edge. Straight tailplane set near to the top of the fin
Variants: Two basic versions, the ATR 42-200 and -300, the latter with increased payload/range. ATR 42-F is a version with larger port-side door; ATR 42-R has a rear fuselage loading ramp. ATR 42-320 has more powerful P&W 121 engines for hot/high performance. The ATR 42-400 has 1,600kW P&WC turboprops, fitted with six-bladed propellers and the Czech carrier CSA became the first airline to take delivery in March 1996. ATR 42-500 improved performance from P&W Canada 127Es driving six-blade propellers. First flown 16 September 1994 and deliveries commenced mid-1995 to Continental Express

A DHC7-100 Dash Seven operating out of London City Airport. *Peter R. March*

The ATR42 has a high-set wing, distinctive shaped fin and rudder set near to the top of the fin. *Daniel J. March*

Bombardier De Havilland Dash 8

Twin turboprop regional airliner
Basic data for Dash 8 Series 300B
Powerplant: Two Pratt & Whitney Canada PW123B turboprops of 1,865kW (2,500shp)
Span: 90ft 9in (27.43m)
Length: 84ft 3in (25.68m)
Max Cruise: 327mph (527km/h)
Passengers: 56 with two crew
First aircraft flown: 20 June 1983 (DHC-8-100); 15 May 1987 (DHC-8-300)
Production: By mid-1996 some 270 Series 100 and over 109 Series 300 delivered and a further 10 Srs 100s and 14 Srs 300s on order
Current service with: Air BC, Ansett New Zealand, Bahamasair, Bangkok AW, British Airways/Brymon, Canadian Regional AL, Contactair, Eastern Australia AL, Great China AL, Hamburg AL, Horizon Air, Sunstate AL, Tyrolean AW, Wideroe, Zhejang AL and many US commuter airlines
Recognition: Narrow profile turboprops set underneath high-set, narrow chord, unswept wings. Circular fuselage section which sweeps up to a broad, slightly swept, rectangular fin and rudder. Dorsal extension reaches forward to the trailing edge of the wing. Straight tailplane set on top of the fin. Streamlined nose with a continuous line down from the cockpit
Variants: The Series 200 is a higher-powered version of the Series 100 with P&WC PW123 engines. Series 300 has a longer (11ft 6in) fuselage to accommodate up to 56 passengers, and Pratt & Whitney PW123 turboprops. The Dash 8M is a military version of the Series 100. A combi version has a large inward-opening door for cargo loading. The Series 400, seating 70 passengers was launched in June 1995. Powered by two 3,598kW PW150 turboprops, and capable of cruising at 647km/h, certification is scheduled for 1998

Fokker 50

Twin turboprop regional airliner
Basic data for Fokker 50-100
Powerplant: Two Pratt & Whitney Canada PW125B turboprops of 1,865kW (2,500shp)
Span: 95ft 1.75in (29.00m)
Length: 82ft 10in (25.25m)
Max Cruise: 332mph (535km/h) at 20,000ft
Passengers: Maximum 46-58 plus two crew
First aircraft flown: 28 December 1985
Production: Over 190 delivered to 24 airlines by mid-1996. Fokker bankrupt on 15 March 1996 with 65 aircraft on order
Recent/current service with: Aer Lingus Commuter, Air UK, Ansett Transport Ind, Austrian, Avianca, Crossair, Icelandair, Kenya AW, KLM Cityhopper, Lufthansa Cityline, Luxair, Maersk, Malaysian AL, Philippine AL, Rio Sul, SAS, Sudan AW and Tyrolean AW
Recognition: Little different from the F27-500 from which it is derived. Twin turboprops set below the high, straight wings. A slender, oval section fuselage with a pointed nose and tail. A tall fin and rudder with a large dorsal extension. The small tailplane is set either side of the base of the rudder. Fokker 50 has smaller rectangular cabin windows than F27-500.
Variants: The Series 300, introduced in 1993, is a 'hot and high' version. The Fokker 60 is a utility version with 1.62m fuselage stretch, four having been ordered by the Royal Netherlands AF

A stretched version of the Dash 8, the series 300, operated by Brymon Airways/British Airways. *Peter R. March*

The Fokker 50 looks very similar to the earlier F-27, but its new powerplant and propellers make it readily recognisable. *Peter R. March*

Gulfstream Aerospace Gulfstream IV

Twin-turbofan long-range business and corporate transport

Data for Gulfstream IV

Powerplant: Two 61.6kN (13,850lb st) Rolls-Royce Tay Mk 611-8 turbofans

Span: 23.72m (77ft 10in) (over winglets)

Length: 26.92m (88ft 4in)

Max cruise: 943km/h (586mph)

Accommodation: 14/19 passengers plus three crew

First aircraft flown: 19 September 1985

History: Introduced as a Gulfstream III with a 54in fuselage stretch, an extra cabin window on each side, a modified wing, glass cockpit and Tay turbofans. It is now being replaced by the Gulfstream IV-SP, with a 'wide body' configuration and longer range. **1993 Gulfstream IV**, an improved, higher weight version introduced in 1993. **SRA-4** is the special missions version of the Gulfstream IV. **C-20G** is the passenger and cargo transport for the US Navy and features a large cargo door and convertible interior. Special mission versions are in service for Electronic Surveillance/Reconnaissance, Maritime Patrol, ASW and Medical Evacuation. **C-20-**USAAF version. Currently 219 Gulfstream IVs are registered as corporate aircraft.

Recognition: Swept wing with pronounced winglets. Wings low-mounted in slight bulge under fuselage, half-way along under fuselage. Slim oval fuselage with six oval windows on each side and front entry door on port side. Two pod mounted engines, set high on each side of rear fuselage. Large cowlings. Rear fuselage tapers to a point. Swept fin and rudder and swept 'T' tailplane.

Saab 2000

Twin turboprop regional airliner

Basic data for Saab 2000

Powerplant: Two Allison AE2100A turboprops of 3,095kW (4,152shp)

Span: 81ft 2.75in (24.76m)

Length: 89ft 6in (27.28m)

Max Cruise: 421mph (678km/h)

Passengers: 50 plus two crew

First aircraft flown: 26 March 1992

Production: 33 delivered by mid-1996 with further 10 on order

Current service with: Air Marshall Islands, Crossair, Deutsche BA and SAS

Recognition: Similar to the Saab 340 but with a much longer fuselage. Slim engines projecting forward of the low, straight wing which has six flap runners on the underside. A circular-section fuselage with large fairings at the wing junction. A swept fin and rudder with a dorsal fillet projecting well forward. The tailplane is mounted at the base of fin. External ventral strakes run from the nose to the wing fairing. The cockpit windscreen slopes down to the nose cone in a continuous line

Variants: A passenger/cargo combi version was introduced late 1996

A Gulfstream Aerospace G-1159C Gulfstream IV. *Peter R. March*

Saab 2000 operated by Crossair of Switzerland in special 'Phantom of the Opera' livery.
Andrew P. March

Cessna 172 Skyhawk

All-metal four-seat piston-engined touring/ training aircraft

Basic data for Cessna 172P Skyhawk II

Powerplant: One 160hp (119kW) Lycoming O-320-D2J piston engine

Span: 35ft 10in (10.92m)

Length: 26ft 11in (8.20m)

Max cruise: 138mph (222km/h)

Accommodation: Pilot plus three passengers

First aircraft flown: 1955

Production: 35,773 (including 2,133 French-built F172s). In addition 237 military Mescaleros were built. Production recommenced at Independence, Kansas and first delivered November 1996. Initial models will be trainers.

Recognition: High-wing monoplane with single thick wing braces under leading edge. Slightly tapered wings with squared tips. Tricycle undercarriage often featuring wheel spats. Swept fin and rudder with small dorsal fillet at front of fin. Tailplane set low at rear extremity.

Variants: Cessna 172 a development of the 170 with a tricycle undercarriage; **172A** — Revised swept tail; **172B** — Deeper fuselage; **172D** — Cut down rear fuselage; **172E** — 150hp (111.8kW) Continental O-300; **172I** — 150hp (111.8kW) Lycoming O-320-E2D; **172N** — 160hp (119.3kW) Lycoming O-320-H2AD; **172Q** — 180hp (134.2kW) Lycoming O-360-A4N; **FR172 Reims Rocket** — 210hp (156.6kW) Continental IO-360-D; **R172K Hawk XPII** — 172N with 195hp Continental IO-360-K; **Skyhawk** — Deluxe versions of the 172; **175 Skylark** — powered by 175hp (130.5kW) Continental GO-300-E; **172RG Cutlass** — More powerful 180hp (134.2kW) Lycoming O-360-A4N engine and retractable undercarriage.

De Havilland DH82A Tiger Moth

Single-engined two-seat biplane trainer

Basic data for DH82A Tiger Moth

Powerplant: One 130hp (97kW) de Havilland Gipsy Major I or 120hp (89.5kW) Gipsy III piston engine

Span: 29ft 4in (8.94m)

Length: 23ft 11in (7.29m)

Max cruise: 93mph (150km/h)

Accommodation: Two seats in tandem open cockpits

First aircraft flown: 26 October 1931

Production: 7,000+

Recognition: Biplane of equal span with slightly swept wings. Twin open cockpits with small windscreens. Fabric covered fuselage and wings. Distinctive de Havilland-shaped fin and rudder.

Variants: The all wood construction DH82B Queen Bee was built for the RAF as a radio controlled target aircraft. The four-seat cabin Thruxton Jackaroo was constructed from ex-RAF Tiger Moths; **DH82C** — as DH82A, built in Canada with enclosed cockpits.

A Cessna Skyhawk F172E featuring typical wheel spats. *Peter R. March*

The DeHavilland DH82A Tiger Moth. *Peter R. March*

Piper J/3C Cub/PA-18 Super Cub

Single-engined tandem two-seat high wing light aircraft

Basic data for PA-18-150 Super Cub

Powerplant: One 150hp (112kW) Lycoming O-320 piston engine

Span: 35ft 4in (10.76m)

Length: 22ft 7in (6.88m)

Max cruise: 115mph (185km/h)

Accommodation: Two tandem seats

First aircraft flown: 1938

Production: Civil 14,124; Military (L-4) 5,673

Recognition: High-wing tube and fabric monoplane. Twin V-struts to wings. Equal chord wings with rounded tips. Braced fixed taildragger undercarriage with cross bracing between wheels. Pointed fin and rudder. Elliptical tailplane. Earlier models have uncowled cylinder heads

Variants: **J/3 Cub** — Original version with uncowled cylinder heads; Continental, Lycoming or Franklin engine of various horsepower ratings between 50 and 100 (37.3-74.6kW); **J-3C-65 Cub Special/PA-11 Cub Special** — Postwar versions with 65hp (48.5kW) Continental A-65 engine; **PA-18 Super Cub** - Introduced in 1952 with Continental C-90; last production version featured a 150hp (111.9kW) Lycoming O-320 piston engine; **Piper PA-18-150 Super Cub** - production resumed in 1988

Robinson R-22

Light utility and pilot training helicopter

Basic data for Robinson R-22 Beta

Powerplant: One 160hp (119kW) Lycoming O-320-B2C piston engine

Main rotor diameter: 25ft 2in (7.67m)

Length: 28ft 9in (8.76m)

Max cruise: 110mph (177km/h)

Accommodation: Pilot plus one passenger/student

First aircraft flown: 28 August 1975

Production: 2,200+

Recognition: Small cabin with large glazed nose area. Twin side doors with windows. Faired main rotor head with twin-bladed main rotor. Enclosed engine. Tubular rear fuselage from upper rear of cabin. Small dorsal and ventral fin at fuselage extremity. Two-bladed rear rotor on port side

Variants: **R-22** — Original model; **R-22 Alpha** — Improved R22; **R-22 Beta** — Current production model with higher powered Lycoming O-320-B2C; **R-22 Mariner** — float version; **R-22 IFR** — equipped with flight instruments for helicopter IFR training; **R-22 Agriculture** — equipped with spray system

A Piper J/3C-65 Cub. *Peter R. March*

A Robinson R-22 Beta operated by ICV Ltd. *Peter R. March*

Sikorsky S-76B

Twin-turbine offshore support, business transport and corporate helicopter

Basic data for S-76B

Powerplant: Two 732kW (981shp) Pratt & Whitney Canada PT6B-36A turboshafts

Main rotor diameter: 13.41m (44ft 0in)

Length: 16.00m (52ft 6in) (rotors turning)

Maximum cruise speed: 269km/h (166mph)

Accommodation: Executive four/eight passengers plus two crew

First aircraft flown: 22 June 1984 (MkII) 1977 (Mk I)

Production: Designed for offshore support, business transport, medical evacuation and general utility purposes using technology and aerodynamics based on those of the UH-60 Black Hawk. In addition to USA it has been exported to China, Germany, Japan, Netherlands, South Korea and the UK. **The S-76 MkII remains in production. The S-76 Utility** and **S-76B** have the PT6B engine. The **S-76C**, that first flew on 18 May 1990, is powered by two 539kW (723shp) Turboméca Arriel 1S1 turboshafts. **H-76** is the armed utility model named **Eagle** and the H-76N a naval variant. A number are in use as corporate helicopters

Recognition: Four-blade main rotor with high twist and varying section. Four-blade cross-beam tail rotor on port side. Twin engines above cabin. Long sleek fuselage. Retractable undercarriage. Four windows, of varying shapes, on each side of fuselage